THE

Word Wasp

A Manual for Teaching the Rules and Structures of Spelling

Harry Cowling B.A. Hons.

Published in the year 2000 by
H J Cowling
Pudsey, West Yorkshire

ISBN O-9538714-0-1
Pilot Impression July 2000

First Edition October 2000

Photocopying

The underlying reasons for poor literacy skills are educational, social, political and some would say psychological and genetic. It is a matter of complete indifference to the individual with the problems: for these people the problem is deeply personal. The Word Wasp is for the individual student. It is an unassuming text which teaches spelling skills without recourse to patronising gimmicks and childish graphics. It is for those students who aspire to sit alongside their literate peers and share the same opportunities without drawing undue attention to their problem. The Word Wasp is their record of achievement. Some students will learn faster than others therefore it is a necessary requirement that each individual has their own book.

Experience has also revealed that many teachers take it upon themselves to form ad hoc programmes using parts of one programme in the hope that it will complement another. The Word Wasp stands on its own and its effects will be diminished and not strengthened by photocopying.

Photocopying will not be permitted under any circumstances.

Acknowledgements

I would like to thank:

Jenna Conlon: she had to be nailed to the table to teach her but she was well worth the effort.
My students **Mike Harvey** and his daughter **Tracey** both helped in the early and continuing development of The Word Wasp.
Christine Gilligan was the first adult that I taught with my early pages. She showed great patience and one day I hope to finish the job that we both started.
Neil Hawes, Julie Storey and Darren Peel also gave much assistance and entertainment during the early development of the text.
Claire Gilligan proved to be a good teacher. She provided me with the proof that The Word Wasp could be used with children as well as adults.
David Brearley deserves a special thanks. He arrived shortly after my Applemac and, fortunately, he never went far away. Without his contribution The Word Wasp would be a long way from the finished product and the Applemac might well have been thrown from my office window.
Keith Taylor was instrumental in guiding me through the labyrinth of programmes and software that make publishing a minefield. He stood by me at a time of crisis in my life. Thanks Keith for all your past support and good luck for the future.
Major Michelle Claridge AGC (ETS) saw the potential of the Word Wasp and was largely responsible for its adoption by Army Education and Training Units: a bold step that others have since followed.
David Hurst of Beeston for his illustration of The Word Wasp used in our advertising.
Dr Jean Alston for her advice on handwriting and her support and faith in both my methods and motives.
My children, **Nicola, Annie** and **Andrew** for living with the 'bear'.
Nicola Dickinson and **Stuart Lupton** for their advice on the structure of the text.
The **Regent Public House** Pudsey for providing me with an oasis in my driest and darkest hours.

To Marie for the Support the Wisdom and the Love.

"If one tells the truth, one is sure, sooner or later, to be found out."
Oscar Wilde

If you just want to teach then move to page 1; follow the instructions in the coaching boxes and get on with it!

Who Needs The Word Wasp?
Any individual with literacy problems including those diagnosed as dyslexic.

Is there a recommended age group? My youngest student was eight years old; the oldest fifty-four. The Word Wasp is a structured system which requires all students, adults and children, to start with the basic letter sounds. It progresses from these sounds embracing a comprehensive range of complex words from 'lock' to 'loquacious'.

Does my student have to be a good reader? No! The coach needs to have reasonably good reading skills. A structured reading programme will improve spelling. A structured spelling programme will improve reading. The Word Wasp does not assume that these skills are mutually exclusive.

Is it possible for adults to miss out the early exercises? Definitely not! The Word Wasp is an integrated system the foundations of which are the basic sound patterns of English. The exercises are linked from the beginning of the text to the end. Miss out any exercise and the result will be frustration.

Can anyone use The Word Wasp? The Word Wasp was designed for adults and children utilizing the experiences of those adults who still remember the problems they encountered as children. The test coaches for The Word Wasp were not teachers. Housewives, office and factory workers, students and the unemployed have used The Word Wasp successfully. Parents and non-teaching assistants can use it without difficulty. Classroom assistants need only be monitored; leaving hard-pressed teaching staff to get on with other classroom business. Parents can use the book in conjunction with teaching staff.

Structure or Word Recognition

Teaching children to read and spell successfully is a rewarding experience. Teaching adults to read and spell successfully is both rewarding and enlightening. Children are often overawed by the presence of adults and often too stigmatized by past failure to express their doubts or ask questions. My most earnest efforts to teach children to spell met with limited short term success as did my attempts to teach dyslexic students a limited Shakespearean experience through word analysis and word recognition exercises.

One of the elements of the teaching methods employed to achieve that partial success was phonemics. It was particularly successful with adults. Children also, seemed easier to handle when they were dealing with structures. Teachers of reading will be all too familiar with the infectious yawns of struggling children. Word-building was less likely to stimulate the nose-picking, yawning and general mayhem of other methods and, gradually, in my private teaching, I began to place more emphasis on word building than other methods.

Under guidance from others whom I considered at the time to be experts, I taught spelling by any means available: mnemonics, rhymes, over-teaching and finger tracing. My methods, and theirs, were all about memorizing and recognizing generically unrelated words.

When it came to teaching someone particularly close, an adult member of my own family, I was allowed for the first time to concentrate solely on the structure of the language with as much time as was necessary. The results were astounding. Using nothing other than phonetics and rules my student advanced at a rate so fast that I feared the effects would be psychologically damaging. However, although my student's reading age advanced dramatically, the same success could not be matched by my teaching of spelling although spelling had been improved generally as a result of the word building.

My spelling method was an adaptation of that which I had been taught. I had been convinced by others that spelling could not be taught to dyslexic students. In fact, I had been convinced that anybody with literacy problems would not be able to learn to spell. I believed that the only words that could be taught were those so often used that they would be written as a motor response, not unlike someone playing 'chopsticks' on the piano.

Initially, my adaptations showed progress but eventually, like the system I had been taught, which was based on the 1000 most used words, it was destined to fail. The common complaint from any of my students was " I am running out of room". Ignoring these apposite remarks I applied more complex mnemonics and taught them more frequently. It wasn't until I was struggling to remember the mnemonic which I had been using to teach a certain word that I realized the total futility of trying to remember a mnemonic or a shape for every word. A small dictionary contains over 70,000 entries! To attempt to teach as little as five percent of that figure would be a disastrous undertaking.

History and structure

Our written language has developed over thousands of years. It is the means whereby we communicate the structures and meaning of speech to others in the absence of the speakers of that language through written symbols. In spite of the diverse cultural, social and national origins of our language its structures follow rules which must be learned before we can communicate in written form. The building blocks of any language has to be the 'sounds'. The mortar which binds them is the rules; a knowledge of grammar allows us to become the architects of communication. The basic sounds are organized in our alphabet, we then construct further sounds by combining letters which broadens the sound base of our communication. We push and weave them together to form words.

Special Needs Teachers will have noticed that many children with weak literacy skills show remarkable skills in playing draughts, chess or using construction sets. There are others too traumatised and alienated by their misery to show any expression other than anxiety or disruptive behaviour.

The moves of the court pieces on a chess board can be likened to those of vowels in our language. Why is it then, that many people believe that we cannot teach the construction of English spelling by the rules of the language itself? Why is it supposed that the shape of a word is more important than the structure of the sounds and rules that formed it?

The answers to these questions some would have us believe are epistemological, scientific, or philosophical and perhaps buried somewhere in the underlying agenda of the Plowden Report. I believe that the answer lies within these areas but politics too has a role to play. I would like to say more but this is not the forum to do so.

In this text, the framework of its approach to spelling is the use of the sounds and rules of English spelling. There is a place for mnemonics and 'look and say' but they play a minor role in the teaching of exceptions and only when the broader range of spelling and reading has been taught.

Those students who finish this text will have their spelling ages, and as a consequence their reading ages, advanced dramatically.

There are those amongst the Special Needs establishment who will throw up their hands in horror and suggest that my system is too pedagogic and too structured. They have had their day! The problem has got worse not better. Students who have been taken through The Word Wasp have had their lives transformed: the curse lifted.

The Word Wasp is about English and the application of its structures and rules. It owes no allegiance to any other purported method of teaching other than those which stem from the language itself. It deems all students equal. It makes no distinctions. Some students, particularly those who have been taught to read through word recognition techniques, will be slower to start than others. Some students fear this text because their supplies of self-esteem have been exhausted through years of failure. No one student will learn at the same rate as another but all will learn and learn well.

The Development of The Word Wasp and Special Educational Needs

My confidence in The Word Wasp arises not only from my own experience of using it but from the experience of others who have used it with both adults and children. Housewives, electricians, printworkers and students have been test coaches for The Word Wasp. This is a method developed for the kitchen table so that it will complement Special Education Needs in schools. Specialist training is not needed. Classroom assistants and parents with the ability to read can use this book successfully.

Good spelling skills cannot be acquired by memorising lists of unrelated words. My older students provide me with an inexhaustible supply of horror stories concerning lists of words to be spelled by Monday mornings. Detentions and other punishments were one price of failure. Ridicule and shame were others. One student told me how she laboured over spellings every weekend and always managed to achieve the acceptable level of eight out of ten until the teacher, for the sake of perversity, decided to ask the spellings in reverse order. She failed miserably to spell all but two correctly.

The Method

The Word Wasp begins by teaching students to spell simple sounds. It never ceases to amaze me that so many students, adults included, cannot spell the basic sounds of our language. From simple sounds it moves to simple words. Many students spell only that which they hear and many sounds are barely audible. The word 'ducts' will be heard as 'ducks' by poor spellers because the letters at the end are blended into one amorphous sound. The Word Wasp emphasises every letter and coaches will be taught to articulate words for spelling. Students are invited to read words and passages in order that they can see, hear, and build the structures and rules of our language and make a necessary link between spelling and speech.

The rules that operate the words in our language are introduced in gradual steps and each step is woven into the structure through the various exercises. The mechanisms for teaching the spelling of difficult words are constantly repeated.

Good spelling cannot be achieved without some knowledge of basic grammar. The difference between the incorrect spelling 'riskt' and 'risked' is the knowledge of simple past tense. How many teachers have seen students with weak literacy skills spell the word 'bothered' as 'botherd'.

The Word Wasp teaches all these skills slowly and carefully. The pronunciation columns and passages do not contain every skill. It is not presumed that every skill needs to be taught. This text provides a springboard for learning spellings. Hundreds of words will be learned directly as a result of using this text: significantly more than any other method because it does not rely on memory training techniques. The Word Wasp invites the student to look for the patterns in our language. These patterns are learned by the student as they become confident with a language which to them has always appeared as a frustrating enigma.

Before using The Word Wasp your student will have believed that every word had a unique structure and pattern. They will have poor reading skills by comparison with others. Many will have struggled against impossible odds to achieve a sustainable level of literacy: a level which has given them credibility in a world of literate people, but that level of literacy will not remove the fear of being 'discovered'. That fear and the ignorance which so often accompanies it are the enemies that The Word Wasp aims to destroy. This is an angry little book.

Harry Cowling

Some Thoughts on the Pilot Edition.

For all its minor flaws, the Pilot Edition of The Word Wasp has proved, without doubt, to be an outstanding success. Above all else it has shown that literacy can only be achieved by a knowledge of the rules and structures of our language.

It has been used with students who have had all manner of labels attached to their problems. The Word Wasp has shown that these conditions, if they have any credibility at all, are secondary to one. That problem is one of alienation from the core of all our social behaviour: **language!**

Since the implementation of the Plowden Report almost forty years ago, successive generations have become disenfranchised from the means of communication and successive governments have failed to deal with the problem. All have maintained that education has been a priority but their futile attempts to remedy the situation have only succeeded in making the problem worse.

Millions are spent on 'sound bitten, schemes which have yet to provide evidence of anything but short term success. They are doomed to fail because they suggest that the problem lies within the students themselves. They rely heavily on memory training and word recognition techniques. The Word Wasp stands diametrically opposed to such ideas.

To those who say that students cannot be taught these rules; the reply must be that students were taught by the rules for centuries and if you don't know them then its high time you learned. To those who say that the Word Wasp is teaching students to "bark at print" the reply is this:

Students of The Word Wasp will ask what a word means and not ask what it says. Students of The Word Wasp can read just as well as they can spell. The Word Wasp gives students the tools to do the job!

The Word Wasp is under constant review. Every day it is manipulated by students who teach the author better ways to teach the rules of our language. It is a truly student based text.

I make no apologies to those methodologists, educational theorists, government bodies and other organizations and institutions to which my comments are aimed. The problem is beyond such petty protocol. This is, more than ever, an angry little book.

Harry Cowling September 2000

What Do I Need?

1 A moderate ability to read the English language.

2 Paper: A broad-lined paper helps students with poor handwriting to control their rambling pens and it will assist in the development of better handwriting. Narrow-lined paper inhibits the natural movement of the hands and may result in the development of an inhibited style. If your student's writing is very bad you may use two lines of a narrow-lined paper: by taking every alternate line on the paper and going over it with a pen you will achieve a good broad writing line with a fainter guideline which will act as a marker for the top of the lower case letters. The writing may be larger than is necessary but you will be able to read it. Better to scale good handwriting down than bad writing up!. Divide each lined sheet of paper into four columns . Always put the date on the top of each sheet.

3 Pen/pencil: The ballpoint pen proliferates because it is cheap and readily available but it has never assisted the development of better handwriting. Finely pointed, fibre tipped pens will break easily. Legibility is crucial; therefore it is suggested that a good HB pencil, with a point sharpened moderately, is used until your student's writing improves. You will notice a continuing gradual improvement in your student's writing. When you are satisfied that a significant improvement has been achieved you might like to take the opportunity to buy your student a fountain pen. The coach should use a black ballpoint to mark the book.

4 Patience: Dyslexic students, both adults and children, need their confidence building. Never, under any circumstance, criticize a student's lack of skill. The onus is on the coach to teach these skills. Coaches are not superior to students. A coach should inspire confidence without being overbearing or patronizing. The function of this book is to teach both literacy through the structure of English spelling and to teach coaches how to teach spelling. The coach is a student too and, as the book progresses, both student and coach are invited to read instructions as part of the exercise. Follow these guidelines and you and your student will reap a lifetime's reward.

Note: If your sole interest is coaching, just use the coaching boxes and ignore the 'Other Information' sections.

Instructions:
Marking the exercises
Look For two consecutive (together) ticks!

Day	8	9	11	12	13	
Month	4	4	4	4	4	
Spell						
aft	/	.	/	.	/	no
eft	/	.	**/**	**/**		yes
art	.	.	/	.	/	no
oft	**/**	**/**				yes

The example above shows the pattern of ticks required before a student's spelling can be considered as consistent enough to leave and move on. The column has been completed when each word has two consecutive ticks

Daily exercise begins by placing the date in the first column of the exercise. The example on the **page opposite** shows that column one was undertaken on August 2nd. The next exercise session followed on August 4th and then the 7th and 8th respectively. Place the date at the top of the column before you begin. Work down each dated column, ticking or dotting each word as required. Progress made on the first day is shown by the hand holding the pen. **Spell or Pro:** The white columns are for your student to read and pronounce in his/her normal manner of speech unless directed otherwise. The blue spelling columns are for the coach to read to his/her student. The blue background and italic print are to prevent easy visual access to the spellings. A postcard will assist!

How long should a lesson be?

Between 20 and 40 minutes a session is usually enough. It isn't necessary to use the book on a daily basis but the more often you work with a student; the faster her/his progress will be. Much depends on your student's writing ability. Lined paper is preferable (See page 1).

Column 1 ✍

Day	2	4	7	8	
Month	8	8	8	8	
Pro					
scr	/	.	/	/	
shr	/	/			
squ	/	/			
squid	/	/			
spr	.	.	/	/	
str	/	/			
shr	/	/			
sprint	/	/			
thrip	/	/			
split	/	/			

Column 2 ✍

Day	2	4	7	8	9
Month	8	8	8	8	8
Spell					
spot	/	/			
skin	/	/			
bra	/	/			
brin	/	/			
bliss	/	/			
dross	/	/			
cram	/	/			
fret	/	/			
slush	.	/	.	/	/
throb	/	/			

Column 3 ✍

Day	2	4	7	
Month	8	8	8	
Spell				
brat	/	/		
thrift	.	/	/	
smug		/	/	
blend				
strap	/	/		
thrash	/	/		
splash	/	/		
grit	/	/		
grip	/	/		
glass	/	/		

Column 4 ✍

Day	2	4	7	8	
Month	8	8	8	8	
Spell					
croft	/	/			
smug	/	/			
twist	/	/			
twill	/	/			
bless	/	/			
flesh	/	/			
flash	/	.	/	/	
struck	/	/			
shred	/	/			
split	/	/			

Do not attempt the same column twice in the same day: one attempt for one tick or dot!

Never allow a student to start a column that he/she will be unable to finish before the end of the lesson. A longhand script (joined-up writing) is preferable to printing but if the coach is unable to read the spellings then the student **must** print the words. The coach needs the book, some scrap paper and a pen; the student needs a pen or pencil and paper.

These are vital exercises. Undoubtedly, some coaches will believe that their students do not need to learn these sounds. Those coaches will fail and their students will suffer as a consequence. My early failures to achieve the desired results, particularly with adults, stemmed from the mistaken belief that these basic sounds had made their way into a student's intellect by 'osmosis'. Describing them as 'baby sounds' fosters the belief that they form part of a genetic development much like the development of milk-teeth. Nothing could be further from the truth. Avoid presuming anything about a student's early development.

The letter 'x' is dealt with later.

Coach:

Ask your student to read and pronounce the sounds on the opposite page. The sounds are **a** as in **a**pple, **b** as in **b**at, **d** as in **d**og. Do not believe that these early exercises can be avoided. Every adult and child taught successfully by the author started here. These sounds form the foundation blocks of our language. Use the grid below to establish the correct sound. Emphasize the use of the tongue when demonstrating **th as in then.** **Vowels are** highlighted in red letters. Your student must say **'vowel'** and then give the proper pronunciation of the letter which will be **a** as in **a**nt etc...

a A	b B	c C	d D	e E	f F
ant	ball	cat	dog	egg	fog
g G	h H	i I	j J	k K	l L
gum	hat	ink	jam	kiss	lemon
m M	n N	o O	p P	qu Qu	r R
mud	nail	orange	pet	queen	rat
s S	t T	u U	v V	w W	y Y
sock	top	up	vet	wasp	yes
z Z	ch	sh	th	th	ck
Zebra	chip	ship	then	thin	lock

Day				Day				Day				Day			
Month				Month				Month				Month			
Pro				Pro				Pro				Pro			
a				sh				u				d			
f				h				v				qu			
g				o				z				th			
l (L)				j				y				a			
b				c				i				m			
c				k				o				l (L)			
r				s				u				s			
t				e				t				ch			
v				p				b				z			
u				i				qu				t			
n				m				w				sh			

Coach:

Ask your student to spell the letter sounds on the opposite page: **a** as in **a**nt **or a**pple, **b** as in **b**at, or **b**all, etc. **You must not say:** a as in **a**corn or b as in the word **bee** etc. You must say the letter sounds that have been used in the previous exercise.

Don't forget: **Your student must earn** two consecutive ticks; each tick must be placed on a different day. (see page 3 if you are not sure).

You can be certain that your student is familiar with the sounds when he/she is able to spell them. Avoid letting your student see the columns and, where possible, try and see the spelling as it is written. Left-handed students are difficult to watch but you should be able to see if a word has been spelled correctly on the first attempt.

The letter **L** has been written in both capitals and lower case (small) letters in order to avoid confusion with the letter **i** (I).

In the case of the letter **k** ask your student to write a 'kicking **K**'.

Be prepared, once more, for the sound **th**. In these early stages you must emphasize the use of the tongue. The letters **th** can make two sounds: **hard th** as in **th**en and **soft th** as in **th**in. The **soft th** is often confused with the letter **f**. Use **hard th** to demonstrate the sound and leave the explanation of **soft th** when it occurs in a proper word. You must speak clearly!

Do not attempt the same column twice in the same day: one attempt for one tick or dot!

Follow the column guides. Speak clearly.

Day				Day				Day				Day			
Month				Month				Month				Month			
Spell				Spell				Spell				Spell			
a				sh				u				d			
f				h				v				qu			
g				o				z				th			
l (L)				j				y				a			
b				c				i				m			
c				k				o				l (L)			
r				s				u				s			
t				e				t				ch			
v				p				b				z			
u				i				qu				t			
n				m				w				sh			

Reminder: Ask your student to spell the sounds **a** as in **a**pple **b** as in **b**at etc.

Other Information

More basic sounds introducing ck

The letter combination 'ck' allows a word to be suffixed with 'ed' or 'ing' without invoking the 'soft c' or 'mute e' rules. This will be made clearer as other rules are introduced. Many people with literacy problems have been taught the alphabet names and not the alphabet sounds (usually by well - intentioned parents or friends): a cardinal error! The letter 'm' does not represent the sound 'em' as in '**em**blem' likewise the letter 'r' does not represent the sound 'ar' as in 'car'.

Coach:

Column 1: Make sure you are familiar with these basic sounds which have been formed by sliding together the sounds on the previous page. Remember: Your student will spell that which he/she hears. Your student must know that this exercise is about constructing sounds. Pay attention to pronunciation. **Speak clearly!**

Column 2: Ask your student to form the **c** sound in these elements by using the **ck** combination.

Column 3: The section highlighted in column 3 is very important. Watch carefully! If the letter **m** is written and then the **e** added to the front or just the letter **m** is written then a dot and not a tick has been earned.
The sound **ar** says **ar** as in c**ar**. If your student spells the word **are** then he/she is spelling from association with words and not building sounds. They have earned a definite dot!

Follow the column guides. Speak clearly.

Day						Day						Day	✳				
Month						Month						Month					
Spell						Spell						Spell					
ib						ock						en					
ap						ick						es					
ol						ith						ar					
os						ack						ef					
og						eck						em					
ig						uck						el					
ug						af						ish					
ep						ush						uch					
uf						et						osh					
um						ub						ath					
om						ag						esh					

Reminder: Two consecutive ticks are needed; each earned on a different day.

Other Information

Coach:

These are all real words formed from simple sounds. Invite your student to form/spell the words from the sounds of the letters. The letter **s** has been added to the end of some of them. This can make the sound of the letter before the final **s** very difficult to hear. Say the word **shot** and then **shots** and listen to the difference. The **t** sound is much softer in **shots**. Later this problem will be more acute and the earlier you are aware of it, the easier the problem will be to deal with.

If your student fails to use twin consonants in words like **gull** or **odd** then they must be given a dot. You must tell your student that twin letters make the sound of one letter. It will not be long before the problem is resolved.

Remember: We are spelling by constructing words from sounds. A student who puts an **e** on the end of the word **par** (p**are**) is guessing as a result of familiarity with the word **are**. Guessing the word through familiarity with other words will pose a problem until your student understands the intention of the book which is to teach the structure of the language.

Guessing is out!
Follow the column guides. Speak clearly.

Day					Day					Day				
Month					Month					Month				
Spell					Spell					Spell				
off					tag					mull				
gaff					quit					bells				
par					cob					loss				
rims					sags					rash				
din					mass					sash				
gull					boss					sham				
rack					less					chub				
dock					fuss					shad				
vat					sock					shops				
lop					neck					chops				
sips					lock					chips				
saps					gums					odds				

Other Information

Coach:

More real words containing simple sounds.

Once more, invite your student to form the words from the sounds of the letters that have already been learned.

If your student spells the word **luck** in column 2 using the twin vowel combination **oo (look)**, he/she is spelling from memory and not from sounds learned earlier.

Tackle the problem now!

Your student must spell from the sounds/letters which have been learned in the previous pages and not from the memory of familiar words. The **oo** combination will be dealt with later.

Follow the column guides. Speak clearly.

Day		Day		Day	
Month		Month		Month	
Spell	✗	Spell		Spell	
that		mill		will	
them		chill		well	
cash		check		dell	
moth		luck		dolls	
cars		sell		tell	
dull		gad		lull	
quip		cuff		bull	
bash		than		socks	
sop		dill		tack	
shut		sill		hock	
shock		this		hack	
get		shells		gum	

Day						Day						Day						Day					
Month						Month						Month						Month					
Spell						Spell						Spell						Spell					
this						or						ash						pit					
gulls						for						pass						cap					
fan						bar						moss						pal					
fad						char						wins						gag					
pulls						tar						wish						nap					
kin						pod						wed						posh					
kiss						dip						begs						pun					
kid						far						bill						sub					
sack						rod						mash						tan					
thick						jars						hush						jack					
jar						cam						cot						jam					
bush						peck						shush						lack					

Day				Day				Day				Day			
Month				Month				Month				Month			
Spell				Spell				Spell				Spell			
lush				shod				paths				sash			
fish				shin				with				rots			
miss				chick				yen				lab			
shot				gush				chin				nib			
mush				pack				chop				hats			
chess				bath				tick				logs			
push				lass				rick				hogs			
odd				chum				beck				ham			
add				hiss				mesh				sham			
rich				pun				lap				jot			
such				mess				quell				sums			
rid				ram				tog				suds			

Coach:

The Pronunciation Columns have two functions:

1) To illustrate a particular rule.

2) To hear the full pronunciation of words.

When reading a word for your student to spell **you must pronounce every vowel sound.** In the word **garden** we can only hear the first vowel: **a.** The **e** is unstressed.

You must make sure that all vowels are stressed. It may not sound like the real word but your student will only spell what he or she hears. The pronunciation columns and passages are for you to correct the pronunciation and tie spelling to speech.

The object of the pro columns in this exercise is to show students that to form plurals it is not enough just to add **s**. Sometimes we have to add **es**. The rule is: if the word ends with the letter **s** (bu**s**) or **sh** (di**sh**) then the plural is formed by adding **es**.

Note: The **es** plural is often pronounced like the word **is**. However, we are interested in spelling: The rule for the coach is: **speak for spelling!** In other words: stress the letters, wherever possible, as a basic sound. The letter **e** often makes the sound **i** as in **i**nk but the coach must use the sound **e** as in **e**gg (eg. wish**e**s) when reading the words for spelling. The student must pronounce words correctly in the pro column.

Follow the column guides. Speak clearly.

Day						Day						Day					
Month						Month						Month					
Pro						Pro						Spell					
hit hits						dish dishes						*bushes*					
bit bits						wish wishes						*masses*					
fan fans						bush bushes						*hills*					
dig digs						rush rushes						*rashes*					
wit wits						loss losses						*wishes*					
add adds						boss bosses						*losses*					
rug rugs						pass passes						*bosses*					
bud buds						lass lasses						*passes*					
fill fills						mash mashes						*buses*					
bill bills						bus buses						*gases*					
mill mills						miss misses						*pushes*					
tap taps						kiss kisses						*gushes*					

Reminder: Two consecutive ticks are needed; each earned on a different day.

Other Information

There are exceptions to all rules but it is easier to learn these as such. Students with weak literacy skills see words as having their own individual shape and spelling. The sight of a small dictionary, which can have as many as 70,000 entries, must seem terrifying.

As part of the spelling programme, students are invited to look at the structure of words as they read and pronounce them. Students with spelling difficulties will, invariably, have reading difficulties; getting by as a result of reading familiar words and guessing others from the contextual evidence. Some students will be remarkably good at it!

The exercise on page 23 is an elementary example of many exercises which are designed to make a student focus on the word and not the context. Once a particular structure is learned at the spelling level it is important to back it up at the level of pronunciation; therefore reading too has its role to play in the teaching of spelling. The Word Wasp does not subscribe to the theory that reading and spelling are mutually exclusive skills.

There is an obvious conflict between that which is pronounced and that which is spelled but you can be assured that it doesn't cause a problem.

Coach:

In the first column, apart from those words highlighted, the **ch** sound has a silent **t** before it. Most words ending with a **ch** sound follow this rule.

The silent letter is highlighted in blue.

Your student must not pronounce the t but they must be aware of its presence in order to spell the words in the spelling columns.

There are more columns for this exercise on pages 22 and 23. The phrases in the pro columns on page 23 must be read perfectly to earn a tick.

The plural form of words with a **ch** or a **z** ending require **es** in the same way as **s:**

dish**es** ditch**es** buzz**es.**

Follow the column guides. Speak clearly.

Day							Day							Day						
Month							Month							Month						
Pro							Spell							Spell						
rich							rich							matches						
such							such							patches						
much							much							latches						
attach							attach							catches						
ditch							ditch							fetches						
pitch							pitch							hatch						
patch							vetch							batch						
vetch							hitch							pitches						
hitch							notch							ketch						
notch							patch							ketchup						
latch							latch							thatch						
fetch							fetch							hatches						

Other Information

Coach:

Listen to the sound made by the letters **ch** in the word **punch**. They make the sound we normally think of as **sh** as in di**sh**. This usually happens when the letters **ch** follow the letter **n**.

The following words begin with the letter **k**:

kiss   king   kipper   keep   kid

If a word begins with a **c** sound but is then followed by an **e** or an **i** sound then we must use a **k** and not a **c**.

Follow the column guides. Speak clearly.

Day				Day				Day				Day			
Month				Month				Month				Month			
Pro				Spell				Pro	k before i and e			Spell			
inch				*inch*				kid				*kid*			
pinch				*inches*				kin				*kin*			
winch				*winches*				Ken				*Ken*			
bench				*bench*				ketch				*ketch*			
tench				*tench*				kip				*kip*			
lunch				*lunch*				kit				*kit*			
bunches				*punches*				kiss				*kiss*			
punches				*ranches*				Kim				*Kim*			
ranch				*benches*				keg				*keg*			
hunch				*hunches*				kisses				*kisses*			
finch				*finch*				kick				*kick*			
finches				*pinch*				Kevin				*Kevin*			

Day						Day						Day					
Month						Month						Month					
Pro						Spell						Spell					
inches						*matches*						*batches*					
pinches						*ditches*						*harsh*					
ranches						*latches*						*marsh*					
lunches						*hutches*						*marshes*					
winches						*quenches*						*hisses*					
quenches						*catches*						*benches*					
finches						*thatch*						*torches*					
rashes						*patches*						*pinches*					
mashes						*pitches*						*mashes*					
fishes						*hitches*						*lunches*					
wishes						*hitch*						*bunches*					
itches						*cashes*						*marches*					

Day						Day						
Month						Month						
Pro						Pro						

Coach: Make sure your student reads every part of these small phrases perfectly.

Pack up the lunches.				Ditch the radish.			
Catch the passes.				A patch can vanish.			
Pull the winch.				had lunch with a pest			
Fish for tench.				Polish the benches.			
She catches kisses.				Finish the dishes.			
He fetches dishes.				wishes for kisses			
Will it be so?				Cut the losses.			
Shall we go?				The tar is harsh.			
This is for me.				Marshes can vanish.			
No it is not!				March with a torch.			
We can push pens.				not for this or that			
This rash itches.				not such a bad match			

Coach:

Columns 1 and 2

Your student must read both parts of each element (eg. **ban** followed by **bank**) to earn a tick. **Blends** are sounds made by two letters which we mix together (blend) to form a single sound. To spell them correctly your student must be aware of the sounds/letters which form each blend.

If your student cannot hear the last letter of the words in this column, do not be surprised if he/she spells them incorrectly. Speak clearly and stress the last letter of each word.

This exercise continues on the pages overleaf. Some of the sounds in the words are very difficult to hear and your students may have never heard them before. The **t** on the end of words ending in **ct** such as se**ct** and ta**ct** are little more than whispers. **Make sure your student hears them!** The problem is more acute in words that end in complex end blends such as **nct** in a word like insti**nct**.

This is an exercise in **auditory discrimination** (listening to, and selecting sounds). It is a difficult exercise for many students. The exercise will sharpen your student's listening skills therefore it is vital that you emphasize all the sounds. Be patient!

Follow the column guides. Speak clearly.

Day							Day							Day						
Month							Month							Month						
Pro							Pro							Spell						
tan tank							bon bond							shelf						
ban bank							fon fond							jump						
lan land							far farm							lamp						
ben bend							char charm							self						
len lend							for ford							charm						
in ink							thin think							think						
dar dark							lef left							thorn						
bar bark							lif lift							born						
shar shark							pin pink							thump						
por pork							el elf							shark						
for form							sel self							champ						
raf raft							hil hilt							melt						

Day					Day					Day					Day				
Month					Month					month					Month					
Spell					Spell					Spell					Spell					
end					fund					barn					bulk					
send					tarn					adorn					silk					
rend					cart					attend					milk					
tend					cost					fork					hulk					
fend					lost					lark					sulk					
land					fast					mark					tilt					
band					tart					bump					wilt					
ramp					rasp					chimp					felt					
sand					raft					lump					bolt					
hand					carp					camp					wink					
bond					harp					damp					pink					
fond					corn					sump					port					

Day				Day				Day			
Month				Month				month			
Spell				Spell				Spell			
ict				edict				intact			
uct				tact				infect			
ect				duct				erect			
oct				sect				effect			
inct *				insect				affect			
tect				defunct				consent			
tinct				tent				detect			
funct				elect				contest			
lect				confess				adopt			
unct				distinct				fact			

The first column contains **sounds** not words. **Make sure that your student is aware of this!** Make sure your student hears every letter in these complex end blends: especially **'c'** and **'t'**. Watch out for the words **edict** and **contest**. Students will hear '**edit**' and '**contess**'. Be aware of the words **duct** and **tact**. Your student will want to use the words **tacked** and **ducked**. The use of '**ed**' at the end of words will be explained later. Your student must use the sounds learned previously. * The student who spells this **sound** by spelling the **word 'inked'** is spelling from memory or association and not from the sounds learned in the earlier exercises. **Stop this practice now!**

Other Information
Division of Words for Spelling

The purpose of this syllable division is for spelling. Words are broken down into manageable auditory units.

All variations of split syllables using both open and closed have been tried. The results have shown that some students hear some sounds better than others and the more students progressed the more discerning they became. Syllables with open ends (cv) were problematic with some students. Most students could hear the vowel 'i' at the end of an open syllable. Many students found the vowels 'a' and 'u' difficult to hear in the early exercises but the more they worked through the text the clearer the vowel sounds became.

Splitting the words encourages coaches to stress the relevant vowel sounds, particularly in the final syllable, which tends to be left unstressed.

To those who throw up their hands in horror, the question must be asked: How did *they* learn syllable division or stress emphasis? The answer is without variance: they didn't! In the pronunciation columns, students will be confronted with the same words and they will see the construction of sounds as words and they will place the stress correctly. In the case of words with which they are not familiar, the coach will be invited to help them in much the same way as everyone is taught the rhythm of an unfamiliar word.

Coach:
Divided Words

Some words will be divided for you so that you can give your student clear sounds. Do not treat them as two words. Leave enough hesitation for the separate sounds to be heard clearly but pronounce them together as one word.

Note: This point will be stressed over and over again: It is vitally important that your student constructs the words from the sounds and rules they have learned without recourse to words they might know already.

The sound **ol** will often be spelled **al** or **all** because students will link words with sounds found in other words like **tall** or **all**. Beware of the **w** which will be inserted after a **qu** sound. Adults are particularly prone to **word association**. The earlier you stop this happening the easier your progress will be.

Follow the column guides. Speak clearly.

Day		Day		Day	
Month		Month		Month	
Spell		Spell		Spell	
quit		quilt		inches	
quid		quick		dem and	
quest		quiff		hush	
con quest		re quest		mush	
li quid		quack		var nish	
quip		ashes		tar nish	
equip		shush		self ish	
quench		chunk		bill et	
quill		quell		mill et	
van quish		a qua		pock et	
in quest		quins		rock et	
help		un just		con tort	

Other Information

Received Sounds and Word Division

People with literacy problems, both children and adults, have usually muddled their way through to a level of literacy which is a product of received sounds; a familiarity with some essential words; sheer determination and guile.

I was first made aware of the problem of received sounds when it was pointed out to me that a dyslexic student under my tuition refused to order two breakfasts in a local cafe. It transpired that she couldn't say the word 'breakfasts'. The word she had always heard was 'breakfass' which meant that the plural was 'breakfasses'. She knew the word was wrong but was unable to contemplate an alternative. She had the same problem with many end blends which contained an 's'. She couldn't offer a plural to 'disk', 'fist', or 'mask'.

Coach:

Column 1
In English the letter **e** often forms the sound of the letter **i** particularly in a final syllable and particularly when followed by the letter **t**.

Column 2
Students will spell that which they hear: listen for the sound of the letter **t** in **fists** or the letter **k** in **risks**. These sounds will be a problem for the coach who does not pronounce the words properly in the spelling columns that follow this exercise.

Column 3
Once more, the words have been divided deliberately for you and your student. You must explain that one word has been split into two sounds but they should be pronounced together as one word. These divisions will be phased out gradually as you progress through the book.

Day						Day						Day					
Month						Month						month					
Pro						Pro						Pro					
rock et						cask casks						con diment					
buck et						risk risks						sed iment					
pock et						lisp lisps						pres ident					
coll ect						last lasts						hal ibut					
mark et						mask masks						sen timent					
lim pet						rusk rusks						con tact					
mill et						rust rusts						con fess					
pull et						gust gusts						var nish					
mall et						fist fists						com pact					
fill et						gasp gasps						con test					
sel ect						bank banks						dark ness					
con tort						form forms						car pets					

Reminder: Two consecutive ticks are needed; each earned on a different day.

Other Information

Coach:

More Difficult End Blends

Your student will have problems hearing the **s** sound on the end of some of these words. You must ask them to listen carefully.

Some words have been repeated from previous exercises. They are there to remind students that **e** can say **i** : e.g. **rock et**.

Be prepared to hiss!

Follow the column guides. Speak clearly.

Day				Day				Day			
Month				Month				Month			
Spell				Spell	* Stress the letter before the final 's'!			Spell			
cult				gasp				sed iment			
in sult				gasps *				con diment			
a dult				cask				res ident			
res ult				casks *				hal ibut			
ob ject				mask				sen timent			
ab ject				masks *				fill et			
coll ect				rust				mill et			
as pect				rusts *				pull et			
im pact				send				mull et			
com pact				sends *				rock et			
in vest				fist				sock et			
in sist				fists*				lock et			
con tact				cusp				dock et			

Other Information

Initial blends.

Initial blends are notoriously difficult for some students to read or spell, particularly if the emphasis of their literacy education has been formed largely by word recognition techniques. This exercise begins to reveal the subtleties and range of phonetic expression.

There are schools of thought which prefer to use the actual sounds as they are formed in the words. The results tend to produce a battery of amorphous sounds barely distinguishable from each other. By using the fully rounded sound, with the emphasis placed on the second consonant, the sound produced is more distinct and easier to recall.

Initial blends form a major plank in the elementary construction of words built from sounds. Once they have been learned, the door is open for more complex constructions and rules for spelling.

Coach:

Initial or Beginning Blends
Columns 1, 2, 3 and 4
Note: If you are unfamiliar with these sounds then get help before you start!

Initial Blends are the sounds made by the blending/ mixing of the two, and sometimes three, letters at the beginning of some words.

Before starting the exercise the coach must read the columns aloud in order to make sure that the student understands what he/she is expected to spell. The coach must always make the distinction between words and sounds. In the first two elements of column 1, the coach will ask the student to spell the *sound* **br** and tick or dot the box before asking the student to spell the *word* **brim**. Continue the rest of the exercise using the same method.

A note on emphasis:

The last letter of a blend should receive more emphasis than the first.

Follow the column guides. Speak clearly.

Day						Day						Day						Day					
Month						Month						Month						Month					
Spell						Spell						Spell						Spell					
br						fr						tw						str					
brim						frog						twin						strap					
bl						gl						sp						spr					
bled						glad						spot						sprat					
cl						gr						sm						scr					
clip						grip						smart						scrap					
cr						pl						sn						thr					
crop						plan						snap						thrust					
dr						pr						sw						shr					
drop						pram						swim						shred					
drag						prod						swill						shrub					
sl						tr						st						spl					
slack						trick						stack						split					

Other Information

This is not the place to introduce the soft 'c' rule. However, too many words would be missed if we left out the blends 'sc' and 'sk'. There are exceptions to the rule: 'skate' and 'skunk'. Introducing these odd words would only serve to confuse.

Coach:

Initial or Beginning Blends
Columns 1 and 2: These columns show complex initial blends in action. Listen carefully to your student's pronunciation. They also show that we use the letter **k,** not **c,** before an **i** or an **e**. Be sure your student recognizes **squ (scw)** as in **squid**.

It is important for the coach to realize that the letters **qu** represent a blend of the letters **c** and **w**.

Columns 3 and 4: These are normal spelling columns.

Note: unusual words: Thrips are well known amongst gardeners as garden pests. There will be many strange words for your student to spell but they are real words and will be used to extend your students ability to use the mechanisms of our language.

Remember that words in the pro column must be pronounced correctly to earn a tick.

Follow the column guides. Speak clearly.

Day				Day				Day				Day			
Month				Month				Month				Month			
Pro				Pro k before 'e' & 'i'				Spell				Spell			
scr				skill				*brat*				*croft*			
shr				skin				*thrift*				*shift*			
squ				skid				*smug*				*twist*			
squid				skep				*scar*				*twill*			
spr				sketch				*stretch*				*bless*			
str				skip				*skin*				*flesh*			
spl				scan				*splash*				*flash*			
thr				scamp				*clash*				*strand*			
sprint				scotch				*grit*				*struck*			
thrips				scar				*grip*				*skill*			
split				scum				*glass*				*split*			
thrush				thrash				*crunch*				*shrink*			

Other Information

Coach:

More Initial or Beginning Blends

Do not forget to stress every letter contained in the words in column 3.

Once again watch out for words like **strict**. If your student spells the word thus: **stricked,** then you can be sure that he/she is not building on sounds; **stricked** is another example of spelling by association with words such as **tricked**. We will teach the sound made by the letters **ed** later.

Follow the column guides. Speak clearly.

Day									
Month									
Spell									
fluff									
brushes									
trench									
tram									
plug									
switch									
dram									
sprig									
shrift									
clinch									
flinch									
clench									

Day									
Month									
Spell									
trend									
drank									
drink									
shrink									
squint									
crush									
crash									
brand									
trunk									
drift									
inch									
grasp									

Day									
Month									
Spell									
im press									
com press									
strict									
con strict									
blushes									
ad junct									
dis trict									
swift									
frond									
plan et									
clashes									
branch									

Day				Day				Day				Day			
Month				Month				Month				Month			
Spell				Spell				Spell				Spell			
corn				em boss				spect rum				med ical			
pulp				Advent				profit				crit ical			
corm				a dept				pros pect				eth ical			
bulb				un just				re tract				ob struct			
filch				a drift				sprock et				ab stract			
cult				em bark				stolid				or dinal			
squint				el vish				stretches				car dinal			
glum				evict				pred ict				or nam ent			
flank				eth nic				con duct				parch ment			
short				up held				instruct				in form al			
shrill				up set				res pect				con script			
splint				in ject				en camp				lig ament			

Coach: Students will not be familiar with these words. This exercise is designed to stimulate the transfer of sounds into spellings and not about expanding your student's vocabulary. It is a tough but necessary exercise. **Get down to it!**

Day				Day				Day				Day			
Month				Month				Month				Month			
Spell				Spell				Spell				Spell	* stress **f**		
im port				clink				squinch				in teg ral			
con sent				crank				pub lish				pess imist			
in dent				stark				tilth				op tim ist			
seven th				in duct				def lect				pen tagon			
inlet				res pect				estab lish				polit ical			
en chant				in tact				plat form				pub lican			
in vest				pep sin				nim bus				elev enth			
vis its				perish				nect ar				twel f th *			
res pond				sac rist				cul prit				wit ness			
un less				revolt				dem ocrat				sub script			
meth od				habits				en crust				invest ment			
tran quil				resist				in habit				with stand			
re flect				de pend				con duct				con form			

Other Information

Coach:

Difficult Sounds

The **ng** word endings are difficult to hear. Taking your student through these words will help your student realize the proper spellings when he/she encounters them in the spelling columns on the pages following this exercise.

You must hear the **d** in ami**d**st. If you hear **lenth** and not **length** then a dot has been earned.

Many people will find these words difficult to hear and say. If your student fails to earn a tick for any or every element it will not be a disaster. **Move on!**

Note:

The exercise will be counter-productive if the end product is anxiety.

Day				Day				Day				Day			
Month				Month				Month				Month			
Pro				Pro				Pro				Pro			
ing sing				ung sung				ong long				ang bang			
distant				rung				amidst				sang			
thing				hatch				song				clang			
wing				flung				crutch				rang			
deposit				refresh				belong				leng length			
sling				slang				clench				strength			
scrimp				brings				thong				stitch			
cling				bung				abrupt				gangs			
impact				support				among				slings			
string				stung				things				longs			
bring				clung				along				king			
sting				lungs				gongs				bringing			

Other Information

Lower Case not Capitals

By choosing to offer advice on this problem at this stage I have allowed both coach and student to familiarize themselves with the pattern of the exercises and develop a necessary rapport. The excessive use by students of capital 'B' and 'D' stems from their confusion of the lower case forms. The same problem sometimes occurs with 'c' and 'g'.

Coach:

Note: From this point on, you may remind your student that you require lower case letters (small ones! Not capitals!) unless they are spelling a proper name. Do not be dogmatic. Watch out for capital **B** and **D** and, occasionally, **G** which is often confused with **C**.

Encourage your student to use a **b** with a tail as shown below. This will help them to make the distinction between **b** and **d**.

When writing the **b** ask your student to start with the tip of the tail and moving the pen/pencil to the point where it meets the downstroke and then down and round in one continuous movement. They can practise writing this letter in their spare time.

Day												Day											Day									
Month												Month											Month									
Spell												Spell											Spell									
thing												thong											slang									
vending												patches											clang									
sing												sibling											bang									
gulf												stretches											clung									
string												throng											gang									
sketch												scratches											length									
bring												oblong											flung									
crunch												prong											strength									
ringing												belonging											stings									
stench												organic											lungs									
singing												gong											fangs									
stinging												clinging											filth									

Coach: The arrows in the exercise below point to the vowels. Ask your student to read each one and make the correct vowel sound: **a** as in an **a**pple, **e** as in **e**gg, etc.

c	a	d	c	e	f	p	v	i	p	c	b	o	n	c	u	p	c	i	t	c	u	w	c	x	a
	▲			▲				▲				▲			▲			▲			▲				▲

Coach: The vowels below are now printed in red. Ask your student to find and pronounce them but this time the vowels must say their name. Their names are **a** as in **a**pe, **e** as in **e**ven, **o** as in **o**ver, **i** as in **i**sland and **u** as in **u**nion. The names of the vowels are often referred to as long sounds or loud sounds. Place a tick in the box underneath the vowel when the student makes the correct sound.

r	i	d	c	a	i	r	c	f	e	c	a	t	l	c	u	e	c	o	c	a	g	a	c	i	o

Coach: Ask your student to say the **sound** of the black vowels and the **name** of the red vowels. Tick the box underneath the correctly pronounced vowel. There are 21 vowels in this exercise of which 9 say their name and 12 say their sound.

f	r	i	t	p	e	o	f	u	m	o	m	i	v	a	k	l	a	t	a	l	o	w	d	a	m

u	h	j	o	e	t	p	u	l	k	g	i	o	l	b	m	h	g	a	p	i	p	z	f	u	a

Day				Day				Day			
Month				Month				Month			
Pro				Spell				Spell			
fangs				*ab sorb*				*hos pit al*			
strength				*crusts*				*dem olish*			
among				*gas kets*				*blem ish*			
amongst				*mus kets*				*adrift*			
length				*defunct*				*spor ting*			
strengthen				*shar pen*				*support*			
singing				*rep ort*				*glints*			
longest				*splen did*				*splashes*			
lungs				*smelting*				*def ending*			
amidst				*in stinct*				*sus pect*			
conquest				*self ish*				*as pects*			
antics				*depict*				*pros pect*			

Pronunciation: As you might expect, words will become longer as you work through the text. Reading requires the same constructional skills to build words from sounds as it does to spell them. The Word Wasp exploits this fact which is why it is vastly superior to those schemes which suppose otherwise. Do not allow your students to guess. The rule is **build or bust!**

Coach:

Silent, Mute or Magic e

The Power of the Vowel Usually Moves from Right to Left

If we add the letter **e** to the end of the word **lop** we form a new word: **lope**.

The **e** stays silent or mute. However, it is still active. Vowels, particularly the letter **e** have the power to influence the sound of other letters, particularly other vowels. In this case the **e** can be described as firing its power through the **p** and into the letter **o** which makes it say its name. Its name is **o** as in bone.

The pro column invites the student to read each line of letters, sounds and words. The vowels which have received the power of the **silent e** are now shown in red print and therefore must say their name. Some people like to use the term **long sound**, others **loud sound** to describe the sound made by the red letters. The term which works with your student is the one to use.

Don't forget: the **e** at the end remains silent.

Note: The twin elements of the first spelling column need to be spelled correctly once only and both elements must be spelled to earn one tick. Ask for **pal** and when that is spelled ask for **pale** and then the tick or dot can be given for both words.

Read and Pro 1

a a al ale gale

e e es ese these

i i ip ipe pipe

o o om ome dome

u u ut ute cute

jump cramp slime

fresh rose pink

bone long clash

			Day						Day						
			Month						Month						
			Spell						Spell						
			pal pale						*convene*						
			cop cope						*these*						
			tap tape						*smile*						
			cut cute						*dale*						
			pin pine						*stale*						
			dim dime						*stole*						
			win wine						*pole*						
			lop lope						*clone*						
			fad fade						*zone*						
			trip tripe						*bone*						
			us use						*fuse*						
			grip gripe						*confuse*						
			rip ripe						*infuse*						

Other Information

Coach:

The first column has the long/loud vowels highlighted in red. In the second column the student must use the **mute e** rule without assistance.

Introducing Key Sounds or Words:

The pro column on page 53 introduces the sound **ire** as in **fire**. It obeys the **mute e** rule but the letter **r** is difficult to hear.

Before you begin the exercise, write the word **ire** on scrap paper and show your student how the addition of **f** makes the word **fire** and **d** makes the word **dire**.

Key Sounds or Key Words will be noted by the letters **KS** or **KW** against the appropriate element.

Follow the column guides. Speak clearly.

Day						Day						Day						Day					
Month						Month						Month						Month					
Pro						Pro						Spell						Spell					
dim						not						*note*						*dis tract*					
dime						note						*fish*						*strand*					
drive						jibe						*trend*						*June*					
grove						spade						*vale*						*vole*					
shift						tope						*shrike*						*divide*					
shale						sole						*lane*						*bane*					
stale						pike						*pike*						*bone*					
froth						larch						*strove*						*alone*					
graft						hake						*strive*						*Mike*					
theme						slime						*thrive*						*Steve*					
smoke						halibut						*cove*						*junk*					
drone						crave						*clench*						*plume*					

Day								Day								Day							
Month								Month								Month							
Spell								Spell								Spell							
prime								flame								glide							
slim								cannot								im pede							
blade								prank								stam pede							
weld								fund								com pete							
crave								funds								com plete							
flitch								sends								gall on							
throne								bribe								chime							
grape								crank								close							
held								broke								en close							
shave								arrive								dis close							
like								adrift								in cline							
slave								jibe								ad here							

Day				Day				Day				Day			
Month				Month				Month				Month			
Pro				Spell				Spell				Spell			
ire *KS*				*de fine*				*condone*				*shire*			
fire				*probe*				*suspect*				*lavish*			
desire				*fire*				*predict*				*divine*			
spire				*scribe*				*conspire*				*effect*			
habit				*entire*				*compose*				*inspire*			
tire				*fulfil*				*compute*				*polite*			
retire				*scrimp*				*desire*				*re quire*			
inspire				*shrimp*				*quake*				*spring*			
require				*admire*				*trombone*				*squire*			
suppose				*ret ire*				*scorching*				*refute*			
admire				*mode*				*until*				*aspire*			
ozone				*trade*				*lem on ade*				*ozone*			

Other Information

Coach:

More Mute E.

Before you begin the exercise, write the word **ore** on scrap paper and show your student how the addition of **s** makes the word **sore** and **m** makes the word **more**.

Don't forget: Do not attempt a column more than once in the same day!

Follow the column guides. Speak clearly.

Day								
Month								
Spell								
ore **K W**								
more								
store								
core								
tore								
snore								
save								
saves								
adores								
sprite								
sprites								
spore								

Day								
Month								
Spell								
pudding								
com bine								
drives								
con trive								
tome								
until								
stores								
con vene								
votes								
gore								
res tore								
es tate								

Day								
Month								
Spell								
con fine								
in vade								
crests								
im plore								
stand ing								
before								
res tores								
thrives								
cones								
clone								
clones								
dec line								

Other Information

Coach:

The two sounds of u.

Your student must understand that the letter **u** can produce two long/loud sounds:

1) **u** as in **flute** or **true** which sounds the same as the word **who**.

2) **u** as in **tube** or **mute** which sounds the same as the word **you**.

Note: Show your student that the word **tube** is formed with a **t** and not a **ch** and make sure that you pronounce the word dune with a **d**. It is easy to form a **j** in front of the **u** which will produce the wrong sound for spelling.

Follow the column guides. Speak clearly.

Day						Day						Day					
Month						Month						Month					
Spell	U cute **Key Sound**					Spell	U moon **Key Sound**					Pro					
mute						flute						sub stitute					
cute						plume						rid icule					
duke						lute						sol itude					
tube						prune						commune					
fuse						true						confuse					
abuse						rude						att itude					
muse						prude						divine					
amuse						crude						immune					
dune						rule						con stitute					
dunes						rules						accuse					
cubes						brute						native					

Other Information

Inevitably, as coach and student progress through the text, less attention will be paid to the coaching boxes. Occasionally, it will be necessary to draw direct attention to a coaching point by placing it at the head of the columns.

Repeated words occur for two reasons: either the author has overlooked the fact that words have been repeated, which is unfortunate but not detrimental to progress, or they have been deliberately duplicated because they have shown to be problematic. The word 'strength' is such a word.

Coach:

See the column guide!

Follow the column guides. Speak clearly.

Day				
Month				

Day				
Month				

Day				
Month				

ure *Key Sound* Coach: Be careful! It is very easy to form a **ch** sound when the letters **ure** follow a **t** as in pic**ture**. Do not form this sound when teaching your students. Make the sound **ture** as in ma**ture** in all words ending **ure** including words like **picture**. You can correct this sound in the pronunciation columns.

Spell				Spell				Spell			
pure				*dis pute*				*rid icule*			
cure				*tribute*				*man icure*			
revolt				*vul ture*				*dest itute*			
stag nate				*salute*				*con stitute*			
singing				*manure*				*in stitute*			
pic ture				*strength*				*ped icure*			
stature				*con trite*				*demure*			
mag nate				*confess*				*procure*			
adult				*secure*				*an imate*			
cul ture				*pollute*				*hab itat*			
den ture				*fumes*				*in trude*			
longing				*belonging*				*con clude*			

Other Information

Coach:

This exercise is the first of many Read and Pronounce sentence grids. **P2** in the small grid on the left of the exercises means that each line has to be read twice successfully.

Tick the box for each successful attempt. Dots and dates are not necessary. Never attempt the same line twice on the same day.

Words in Bold Print:

With the exception of the words in bold print, your student must read every word in a line correctly to earn a tick.

If your student has difficulty with the words in bold print you may read the word for them. However, other words must be broken down into their sounds. Students, having reached this exercise, are just as capable of breaking down words into the sounds and rules as they are of building them. They don't always know they can. It's your job to show them!

Read and Pronounce

Put the cube in the tube and send it as a tribute in gratitude to the **hungry** multitude.

Cure the illness by drinking **plenty** of liquids and go to the store for some more pills.

Defy the vulture and hang up a picture and if in dispute be resolute and **play** the flute.

In the event of bones **being** bent; take a pinch of snuff and some fresh linament and rub

them with relish but do not venture to use the same hands to clean **your** dentures

because if **you** do **they might** set like glue but **you** will be **sure** that **your teeth**

are secure. Strive at length to **regain** strength and take some time or **you may** decline.

Rotten flesh is fine for a vulture, **they have** no **teeth** just hard gums **which they** often

use **when they** consume plums or prunes. I have no desire to restore the fire.

You may venture in the park **when** it's wet or **when** it's dark **because ghosts there are**

not, but my instinct thinks that a distinct mole is often the sole dark mammal in a hole.

Take note of the blokes that sing out of tune and ignore the bells that ring in the dales.

Other Information

Here, There and Where.

My grandfather would have had little difficulty with the following words: 'there' and 'where'. Both words rhymed with 'here' and in some parts of Yorkshire they still do. However, it is not the rhyme but the spelling which can be linked. Each word is about a geographical location and each word contains the word 'here': **here, there, where**. The word 'here' follows the 'mute e' rule and 'silent h' has also been introduced so this is the appropriate place to introduce these words and they will be repeated together again and again.

Coach:

Column 1 (Pro 2) introduces a silent letter **h**. The rule is that **h** is silent after a **w**.

Column 2 introduces the words **here**, **where** and **there**. The word **here** follows the **mute e** rule which we have been dealing with over the last few exercises. Point out to your student that all these words are concerned with places and contain the word **here** and **here** is a place.

Where is a place (somewhere, anywhere, where it happened).

There is a place.

Here is a place.

To spell the words correctly the student must make sure that they contain the word **here**.

Follow the column guides. Speak clearly.

Day						Day						Day					
Month						Month						Month					
Pro Silent **h**						Pro						Spell					
rapture						stale						*quake*					
scripture						stalemate						*infect*					
future						hoping						*arches*					
brine						quintet						*scale*					
w**h**ile						require						*gales*					
w**h**en						shard						*holes*					
w**h**ich						grebe						*poles*					
w**h**ip						glebe						*moles*					
w**h**ale						mere						*voles*					
w**h**isk						here *K W*						*here*					
w**h**ite						there						*there*					
w**h**iff						where						*where*					

Other Information

Coach:

Some of the words in column 3 contain the **sm** final blend. These tend to be medical or scientific terms. Explain that the end blend, notably that **s** before an **m**, makes a **z** sound and with the vowel **i,** the overall sound is more like **izzum**. The **a** with the **sm** final blend makes a sound similar to **azzum**.

Page 66 Read and Pronounce: With the exception of the words in bold print, your student must read every word in a line correctly to earn a tick.

If your student has difficulty with the words in bold print you may read the word for them. However, other words must be broken down into their sounds. The word **ghost (Page 66)** is particularly important for The Word Wasp and the letters highlighted in red will reappear later.

Northern coaches: (Page 67) You may have difficulty with the words **some, become** etc. For spelling purposes, they should share the same vowel sound as **o** in **dog**.

Follow the column guides. Speak clearly.

Day						Day						Day					
Month						Month						Month					
Spell						Spell						Spell					
core						shank						spasm					
deplore						thrift						prism					
store						trunking						or gan ism					
require						adore						spas modic					
before						score						em bol ism					
while						pic ture						pess im ism					
which						cul ture						en dop lasm					
here						en dure						metab olism					
there						more						med itate					
where						sore						op tim ism					
sculp ture						tore						art ichoke					
future						pending						mending					

Read and Pro 2: Introducing ee

Ethel Stritch from West Shoreditch did not like her classmates.

She left her school and **all** its rules for a distant landscape.

There she sits quite **free** of zits, **applying** lots of lipstick

to her lips and **other** bits, while **eating** lemon pancakes.

Coach: Don't forget! You can give help with words in bold letters.

Enigmatic plastic pants are often **seen** on the bottoms of **bees.** They stop them from

stinging men but not so **chimpanzees. Double e (ee)** makes the long **sound of e.**

Coach: Ask your student to take note: The silent **e** has no power in the words **none, gone**, **done**, **some**, **one**, or **become**. Remind your student to use **ee** where necessary on Page 67

It went from here to there.   Has she **gone**?   Did it **come**?   It will take **some** time!

Some went there.   She has **done** it.   The buses are there.   **Are** the jobs **done**?

Words about places such as **there** and **where** **contain** the **word here.**

Question: Are there such things as **ghosts**?

Answer: Only the **ghosts** that **haunt** some **words**!

Day							Day						Day						
Month							Month						Month						
Spell							Spell						Spell		* Ask your student to use **ee** to spell these words.				
site							cute						bee *						
done							amuse						agree *						
one							abuse						agreed *						
none							secure						des titute						
come							while						degree *						
become							which						tree *						
some							shrine						em bellish						
here							erupt						emigrate						
there							rup ture						free dom *						
where							struc ture						neg lect						
are							rap ture						con flict						
ghost							para site						por tent						

Other Information

Coach:

English words cannot end in the letter V.

The mute **e** on the end of words which end with the sound **v** was a way of distinguishing between the letters **v** and **u**. Many years ago these letters were interchangeable. The **e** announced that the last letter of a word was a **v** and not a **u**. It always helps to give reasons and where possible, providing the explanation is not too complicated, you should explain the rule to your students.

A note for Northern coaches only:

When the words **glove**, **love**, **shove** etc, find their way into the spelling columns you should pronounce the letter **o** as the **o** in dog. '**Luv**' might be closer to your accent or that of your pupil and it is perfectly acceptable as part of his/her speech but your student needs to hear the sound in order to spell the word. The author too has a northern accent and appreciates the problem.

Follow the column guides. Speak clearly.

Day						
Month						
Pro						
love						
above						
glove						
dove						
sue						
due						
give						
have						
solve						
shove						
blue						
glue						

Day						
Month						
Spell						
blue						
glue						
true						
clue						
gone						
one						
done						
there						
come						
sue						
none						
here						

Day						
Month						
Spell						
venue						
im bue						
assume						
prune						
presume						
con strue						
while						
when						
which						
have						
con script						
scrip ture						

Day				
Month				
Spell				
in dicate				
absorb				
elas ticate				
ded icate				
estate				
venue				
avenue				
revenue				
chicken				
con tinue				
require				
morbid				

Day				
Month				
Spell				
give				
forgive				
bran dish				
pass ive				
blem ish				
or nate				
requite				
one				
done				
crash				
crashes				
tal ent				

Day				
Month				
Spell				
ob ject				
ob jective				
un due				
in stinct				
in stinc tive				
mass ive				
stress				
stresses				
dress				
dresses				
active				
torment				

Day						Day						Day					
Month						Month						Month					
Spell						Spell						Spell					
commute						*in culcate*						*sub ject*					
mundane						*en grave*						*sub jective*					
frac ture						*structure*						*res pective*					
un til						*lapwing*						*nos trum*					
fulfil						*econ omist*						*cap ture*					
in form						*trans mit*						*im port*					
in form ative						*trans mute*						*inn ings*					
ret inue						*trans pire*						*ill us trate*					
en dure						*trans pose*						*im pulsive*					
fus tigate						*tran sport*						*glob ule*					
in vest igate						*shelve*						*sub sume*					
com pul sive						*con trast ing*						*bloss om*					

Other Information

Coach:

The three sounds of y.

Listen to the sounds of **y** in the following words:

y as in **y**es

y saying **i** as in merr**y**

y saying **i** as in fl**y**

Column 1: Read the column to your student pointing out the three different sounds made by the letter **y**.   After which, the student must complete the exercise in the usual way by reading and pronouncing the words.

The letters highlighted in red depict **y** saying **i** as in fl**y**

Note: The student who begins spelling the word **hybrid** (page 74) with the word **high** is not constructing the word from sounds and rules. Be ready to make that point.

Follow the column guides. Speak clearly.

Day						Day						Day					
Month						Month						Month					
Pro						Spell		y saying **i**				Spell					
sorry						*dignify*						*very*					
yard						*defy*						*sys tem*					
badly						*deny*						*porch*					
nylon						*supply*						*mystic*					
sky						*com ply*						*starch*					
skylark						*pylon*						*stretch*					
happy						*simp lify*						*Holly*					
deny						*edify*						*marry*					
defy						*sat isfy*						*dusty*					
sadly						*sol id ify*						*happy*					
madly						*clarify*						*nylon*					
gladly						*apply*						*frosty*					

Day							Day							Day							
Month							Month							Month							
Spell							Spell							Spell							
yelp							merry							try							
yell							folly							fly							
yard							berry							deny							
yarn							Harry							defy							
yard arm							fifty							spry							
yard stick							twenty							my							
yen							misty							my self							
yes							body							mod ify							
York							sym bol							mag nify							
yet							myth							hy brid							
yank							sys tem							imply							
rule							sorry							rec tify							

Read and Pronounce

Introducing the short cut X

Coach: Offer assistance with words in bold print when and where it is needed.

The **girl** above gave the glove a shove and it fell from above. **Mix** the sticks and send a **fax** to the man from **Halifax**. Take a missive to the **woman** at the **exit** and bring back a reply but try not to terrify the bride inside as she hides from the man from the Inland Revenue who came along the avenue on his bike. Strike it from the records and tell the bloke to indicate where his abode will be **should** he strive to thrive by a stretch of land by the strand. If he **should** shove the shovel for his living he will have sore hands and picture the structure and the **mixture** of **fixtures** that hang from the stand in the kitchen. This **means** nothing to a vulture. It has habits from a distant culture. "Are you sure that this melon is mature?" said the empress to her son who was **inclined** to say nothing **unkind** as he spent his time drinking wine. "I think I will recline and think of things sublime," **said** the son at the time. Use a white whisk to **mix** the **mixture** into a fluffy **texture**. Sitting over there, where the **sea** is blue, seems better than sitting here when the gas bill is due.

Other Information

Before students are introduced to words like 'except', 'excel' and 'excite' they must first be made familiar with the soft 'c' rule which appears on page 182.

Words such as 'excuse' require the 'c' to be sounded as in 'ex / cuse'.

Coach:

Read the following **sound** which seems like a real word and then read the real word:

ecspect = <u>ex<u>pect</u></u>

Read the following **sound** which seems like a real word and then read the real word:

e**gs**am = <u>ex<u>am</u></u>

Refer your student to the diagram on the left and ask him/her to draw it on scrap paper. Demonstrate how each point of the cross represents the four letters.

The letter **x** makes two common sounds in English: **ecs/ecks** (compare tax and tacks) or **gs** as in **exam**, **exhibit** or **exile**.

Work through the Pro columns in the usual way.

Note: You may need to help your student with the words **prove**, **move** and **improve**. They all rhyme which should make your task easier.

Before starting the spelling columns ask your student to use **x** in the appropriate words. Words ending in the letter **x** require **es** to form the plural **(boxes)**.

Follow the column guides. Speak clearly.

Day					Day					Day					Day				
Month					Month					Month					Month				
Pro	x = cs				Pro	x = gs				Using X Spell					Using X Spell				
lacks					eggs					*mix*					*exam*				
lax					exam					*fix*					*exult*				
tacks					exude					*expand*					*exist*				
tax					**gh**ost					*lax*					*exotic*				
vex					remove					*box*					*exact*				
are					exult					*flex*					*existing*				
mix					prove					*relax*					*exile*				
excuse					exact					*vex*					*exude*				
vexing					improve					*crux*					*move*				
expand					exist					*sixty*					*prove*				
extent					where					*convex*					*remove*				
explode					exhume					*ex tract*					*ex hale*				

Day		Day		Day	
Month		Month		Month	
Spell	extend words ending in x with es	Spell		Spell	
box		cortex		Tex as	
boxes		export		next	
fox		equin ox		extend	
foxes		vex		context	
relax		convex		Sax on	
relaxes		thorax		toxin	
extent		expect		ex tinct	
text		toxic		mixing	
vortex		influx		fixing	
textile		max imum		fixture	
mix ture		explode		Mex ican	
flax		ex plosive		fixative	

Day		Day		Day	
Month		Month		Month	
Spell		Spell		Spell	
expose		squire		store	
exclude		expire		score	
tribute		exam		enclose	
inject		strong		explode	
taxes		oblong		hard	
belong		junc ture		lan yard	
one		punc ture		standing	
stride		gone		demand	
polite		come		sports	
ex ped ite		there		elect ron	
ex plicate		become		elect ric	
nav igate		someone		for mal	

Other Information

Coach:

More read pronounce sentences.

This is a regular pronunciation exercise. Every word in a line, with the exception of those in bold print, must be read and pronounced properly to earn a tick.

You may offer help with the words in bold letters. Vowels highlighted in red make their long/loud sound.

Do not expect this passage to make sense. Your student must read and pronounce the words without the aid of contextual clues.

Don't forget: Do not attempt these sentence - lines more than once in the same day!

Read and Pronounce

Continue to take the blue pills and take hot baths and **you** will s**oo**n be back to normal.

Hang the picture by the fire but make sure it does not get t**oo** hot.

It was **cold** by the shore and the wind tore **through** the dunes flicking sand into his

stinging eyes. The **sea splashed** his feet and Steve **was** sorry he was there when he **could**

have been somewhere **warm** and dry like Texas or Mexico.

Do not expose your nose to those winds from the North if **you** are not sure if **you** can

endure the arctic blasts. Take a mixture of tar; black **tea**; some hot rum; six radishes; and

five cloves, nineteen feet of sheep's teeth crushed with three **slices** of grilled eel and feel

much **worse** than you ever did before. Resist the move if you **don't** approve of it.

To improve the **recipe**: remove the teeth and eel and some of the radish then cook together

for twenty minutes at one hundred and fifty degrees. When the smell has gone it will not

be long before you will feel free to sleep on the **beach**. **You** will have red cheeks and

cold hands but a **pair** of gloves, sent with love, will help to improve your latest move.

Take **care** over there where the snakes in the grass compete with the rats and the broken glass.

Coach:

Has it happened? Simple Past Tense: ed

Read the following sentences:

Sue fix**ed** the shelves.

Jack mend**ed** the car**.**

Both sentences inform us that something has happened. Sue is not fixing the shelves at the moment. Sue is not going to fix them in the future: she has already fixed the shelves. The same conditions apply to Jack.

The sound made by the letters **ed** differs in each word. Listen carefully:

The **ed** in mend**ed** sounds a little like the **id** in d**id**.

The **ed** in fix**ed** makes the sound **t**.

To place most words in the **simple past tense** we add the letters **ed** to the end of them.

Column 1: The vowel sounds in these words are given their long sound by the use of the **mute/silent e**. To put these words in the past tense it is necessary to add the letter **d** alone:

plane+d = planed.

However, if we need to put the word **plan** in the simple past tense, adding **ed** is not enough. The power of the **silent e** would still reach the **a** and we would spell **planed** once more.

How to do it!
Column 2: To stop the power of the **mute e** from reaching a vowel we must build a barrier by using another letter: eg. **plan + n + ed** gives us the word **planned** which has a double barrier (**nn**) against the power of the **e**. Explain this to your student. This is why we have double consonants. **Column 2** demonstrates this rule.

Column 3: These words may end in the sound **t** but whatever the sound: the spelling is still **ed**.

Note: Words like ba**ng** and fo**rm** already have two consonants after the vowel to protect them from the **silent e** so doubling is not necessary: ba**ng**ed, fo**rm**ed.

Do not attempt the same column twice in the same day: one attempt for one tick or dot!

Day				Day				Day			
Month				Month				Month			
Spell	silent e + d			Spell	double + ed except for *			Spell	ed sounds like t		
plane planed				plan planned				miss missed			
frame framed				fan fanned				pass passed			
file filed				hum hummed				chase chased			
smile smiled				peg pegged				box boxed			
crave craved				lag lagged				rush rushed			
amaze amazed				sag sagged				push pushed			
pose posed				drum drummed				ask asked			
fire fired				cram crammed				risk risked			
close closed				long longed *				base based			
love loved				pull pulled				wish wished			
shove shoved				form formed *				park parked			
move moved				farm farmed *				mark marked			

Coach: Your student must spell each pair to earn one tick!

Other Information

It might seem easier to have the coach pronounce the past tense form of the word rather than use the '+' symbol but that would defeat the object which is to encourage the student to work out the concept of 'simple past tense'.

Coach:

The spelling columns 2 and 3 require the coach to say a word which must be repeated by your student in simple past tense form: e.g.

1) Coach says "**demand**"
2) Student says "**demanded**"
3) Student spells **demanded.**

The words marked **+ p ed** or **+ n ed** are reminders that the final letter (consonant) must be doubled. Remember to pronounce the word endings **ure** as if they sound like the word **your**!
There is no **ch** in mature, structure, capture, etc.

Do not attempt the same column twice in the same day: one attempt for one tick or dot!

Follow the column guides. Speak clearly.

Day		Day			Day		
Month		Month			Month		
Spell		Spell		Ask for the past tense	Spell		Ask for the past tense
astute		demand +			scratch +		
stop		stretch +			jump +		
include		despatch +			remove +		
stamp		invade +			prove +		
mature		cope +			pinch +		
capture		time +			drench +		
pinch		mature +			improve +		
structure		include +			start +		
drench		grasp +			land +		
shop		mend +			clap+ p ed		
drop		drop+p ed			ban+ n ed		
mend		shop+p ed			trap +p ed		

Other Information

Coach:

The letters er at the end of a word.

The letters **er** make two sounds: in the middle of a word they say **er** as in te**r**m. In this exercise we are concerned with **er** at the end of words where the sound is barely stressed at all. Listen to the sound that the letters make at the end of the following words: moth**er,** butt**er,** dinn**er,** min**er.**

The sound is little more than a grunt: a short puff of air from the back of the throat but we can still spell it! In the majority of cases, where a word ends with this sound, the letters that form that sound are **er**.

Words which are formed from **mute e** take the letter **r** alone.

Column 3 will challenge your students who will want to end the words with the letters **erd**.

The rules for column three are the same as those on page 85: Ask your student for the Past Tense.

Follow the column guides. Speak clearly.

Day								Day								Day							
Month								Month								Month							
Pro								Spell								Spell	+ = ed						
mother								*singer*								*splutter* +							
baker								*drummer*								*batter* +							
driver								*bother*								*hammer* +							
viper								*runner*								*cover* +							
dinner								*boxer*								*shatter* +							
butter								*simmer*								*corner* +							
batter								*spinner*								*gather* +							
mutter								*platter*								*litter* +							
chatter								*splatter*								*glitter* +							
lover								*fluster*								*tether* +							
miller								*hammer*								*foster* +							
miner								*spinster*								*fluster* +							

Day				Day				Day				Day			
Month				Month				Month				Month			
Pro				Pro				Spell				Spell			
bigger				rider				*sister*				*thicker*			
better				backer				*blister*				*thinner*			
lesser				broker				*bigger*				*darker*			
runner				tracker				*better*				*paler*			
seller				letter				*letter*				*winter*			
sender				miner				*other*				*fender*			
fatter				hopper				*mother*				*defender*			
thinner				another				*brother*				*ladder*			
thicker				spider				*matter*				*scamper*			
other				brother				*fatter*				*runner*			
matter				tripper				*lender*				*spider*			
farmer				stoker				*porter*				*banner*			

Day						Day						Day						
Month						Month						Month						
Pro						Spell						Spell						
bother						hacker						pris on er						
bothered						send						line						
withered						sender						lined						
tether						blender						liner						
tethered						cluster						cover						
gather						duster						blistered						
gathered						broker						battered						
shatter						bluster						leng th						
shattered						banker						leng then						
blistered						tanker						leng thened						
clustered						thanked						streng then						
hovered						member						streng thened						

Other Information

Coach:

Changing y at the end of a word.

Words which end in **y** can be extended in much the same way as words which do not, but with one minor difference: we must change **y** to **i** and then add the letters **ed, er** or **es**.

See how the word **carry** changes when it is extended:

carry changes to carr**i** + **ed** to form **carried**
carry changes to carr**i** + **er** to form **carrier**
carry changes to carr**i** + **es** to form **carries**

Demonstrate the above changes made to the word **carry** on scrap paper then begin the exercise.

Don't forget:
Do not attempt the same column twice in the same day: one attempt for one tick or dot!

Day						Day						Day					
Month						Month						Month					
Pro						Spell						Spell					
marry married						*dignify dignified*						*exclude*					
carry carried						*signify signified*						*expose*					
supply supplier						*solidify solidified*						*carrier*					
mystify mystified						*magnify magnified*						*harrier*					
cry cried						*deny denied*						*barrier*					
try tried						*defy defied*						*merrier*					
apply applied						*clarify clarified*						*fresher*					
deny denied						*hurry hurried*						*happier*					
fry fried						*simplify simplified*						*wetter*					
dry dried						*bully bullied*						*expand*					
defy defied						*terrify terrified*						*remove*					
comply complied						*sanctify sanctified*						*improve*					

Day						Day						Day					
Month						Month						Month					
Pro						Pro						Pro					
carry						barrier						glories					
carried						pannier						gloried					
carrier						penny						expecting					
carries						pennies						expected					
ferry						entry						expired					
ferried						entries						desired					
ferries						sentry						flexed					
berry						sentries						complex					
berries						folly						exacted					
lorry						follies						extracted					
lorries						glory						maximized					
story						stories						primates					

Day		Day		Day	
Month		Month		Month	
Spell		Spell	* stress **or** !	Spell	* Stress **er** !
replies		*some*		*injuries*	
marries		*one*		*terri tory*	
carries		*someone*		*terri tories*	
entries		*something*		*liberty* *	
parties		*somewhere*		*lib erties* *	
sentries		*enquire*		*lib erate* *	
bullies		*enquiry*		*lib erated* *	
identifies		*enquiries*		*prop erty* *	
rectifies		*enquires*		*prop erties* *	
flies		*cal ories* *		*col ony*	
spies		*injury*		*colon ies*	
applies		*mem ories* *		*an tidote*	

Read and Pronounce

"There is nowhere to sit in here for the likes of **you**," said the lady in the **first** class seats.

Pennies from **Heaven**, money for old rope, cash on the nose, lots of lolly, makes the

Empress happier, funnier, fizzier and dizzier. Having carried the empty bucket to the

top of the hill Jack refused to carry the full one back down. Jill **was** very unhappy with

Jack's lazy attitude and banged him on the **head** with the bucket. Jack became very

angry at this but he was too dizzy to reply. Jill was **about** to apply a sheet of **brown**

paper to the cut on Jack's **head** but it was too dry. The wettest thing to hand was a flask

of vinegar. This **was** applied and Jack felt a severe pain which did **little** for his temper.

Jill **thought** it was time to go and sprinted down the hill. Jack set off but slipped on the

wet **brown** paper and staggered into the path of a lorry. The lorries brakes were applied

quickly. The driver, unhappy at Jack's seemingly silly antics, punched Jack on the nose

which bled onto his **clean** jumper. When Jack's mother **saw** the dried blood she **was**

sure that Jack had been **fighting** and confined him to the garden for a month. Jill **was**

denied Jack's company and married the lorry driver.

Read and Pronounce

"But there are no more **seats** on the **train** and my feet are killing me," replied the

woman with the shopping bags, "and I'm ever so tired. My arms are dropping off!"

It may seem **strange** but you **should know** that **a** after **w** most often says **o**!

Has **Wally** the **wasp washed** his hands or has the **warm** wind made him lazy?

One must conclude that **wasps** are rude but not so bees that **swarm** on trees.

Was it the **wasp** that **wanted** to chase the **swan** off the **swamp**?

The man with the **warts** from **ward** three went to **war** but **was** back in bed when the

woman said, "To **whom** do these cherries and grapes belong?" "To me," he said with

glee but he **was** too late and before long grape seeds and cherry stones were piled upon

his plate. **Swap** these piles of stones for smiles. Include the man who can **swat** the

flies. A consonant is a letter other than a **vowel**. The **vowels** are **powerful** letters.

The letters **below** are those of **our alphabet**. The red letters are **vowels** and the black

letters are **consonants**.

a b c d e f g h i j k l m n o p q r s t u v w x (sometimes y is a vowel) z .

Other Information

The concept of a letter defying that which a student has already learned ('a' can say 'o') can take some time to instil. Students have already been introduced to the 'ee' sound which is very regular, and proof that one rule works gives heart when students are struggling with a more difficult one.

Hints at the tops of some of the columns are given in order to help students choose the appropriate rule to use. The Word Wasp does not subscribe to the notion that language is a private form of intelligence that must be doled out in ritually earned snippets. Learning is not about guessing the shape of a word from lists of generically unrelated words. Students of The Word Wasp will be assisted as much as possible.

Coach:

The letter a after w and ee.

The letter **a** after a **w** makes the sound **o**. Listen to the sound in the following words:

w**a**s w**a**nt w**a**sh

The sound made by the vowel **a** is the same as that of **o** as in d**o**g.

You have already introduced your student to the double **ee** sound.

The letters **ee** make the one sound. Listen to the sound in the following words:

st**ee**l wh**ee**l gr**ee**d.

Follow the column guides. Speak clearly.

Day				Day				Day				Day			
Month				Month				Month				Month			
Pro				Pro				Spell				Spell			
was				steel				*swarm*				*washing*			
want				sweet				*invade*				*sweets*			
war				feel				*wasp*				*watch*			
wart				keel				*wallet*				*feel*			
ward				keen				*warden*				*water*			
wasp				need				*swamp*				*feeling*			
waft				Leeds				*street*				*sheet*			
swap				seen				*sward*				*keen*			
swan				bee				*swab*				*been*			
award				seeds				*feet*				*deed*			
warm				weeds				*thwart*				*indeed*			
wand				breeding				*wallaby*				*Walter*			

Day					Day					Day				
Month					Month					Month				
Pro	s, z & th ends need **e**				Spell	* Say use **x** to spell these words.				Spell	Remind your student to use double 'ee'			
freeze					*bleeding*					*redeem*				
foxes					*textile* *					*peevish*				
cheese					*steep*					*fleeting*				
boxes					*valve*					*greetings*				
meek					*canteen*					*preen*				
seethe					*involve*					*sheer*				
explore					*freedom*					*keeping*				
breeze					*ghost*					*freeze*				
venture					*coffee*					*breeze*				
sneeze					*toxins* *					*sneeze*				
flee					*toffee*					*squeeze*				
agree					*greedy*					*agreed*				

Day						Day						Day						
Month						Month						Month						
Pro						Spell						Spell						
peeling						*denies*						*second*						
defies						*washing*						*polite*						
meeting						*streets*						*jelly*						
complied						*someone*						*replies*						
agreed						*punctures*						*jellies*						
scorches						*proposes*						*move*						
applies						*revolved*						*prove*						
cheek						*terrify*						*remove*						
move						*in volved*						*moved*						
prove						*sec luded*						*proved*						
lose						*struc ture*						*pedigree*						
peltate						*strength*						*peltate*						

Day						Day						Day					
Month						Month						Month					
Spell						Spell						Spell					
pensive						*desire*						*verbose*					
expensive						*admire*						*comprise*					
adore						*evolve*						*primed*					
revise						*respite*						*above*					
implore						*trite*						*love*					
blend						*contrite*						*glove*					
men thol						*tincture*						*glee*					
update						*steered*						*green*					
packed						*beer*						*closed*					
creeping						*cheer*						*bleeds*					
inspire						*sweeps*						*sheen*					
conspire						*cheek*						*cheered*					

Day					Day					Day				
Month					Month					Month				
Spell	* use y and x				Spell					Spell				
branches					done					ex tricate				
fixed					gone					ex plicate				
ex posed					adipose					con gregate				
ex cuse					ex pel					tox ins				
ex tent					glossed					in tox icate				
ex pand					jetty					rep licate				
ex port					jetties					sun dry				
dep rived					war den					sun dries				
warning					story					con spired				
ward					stories					Wash ington				
warder					awarded					flinching				
syn tax *					wanting					warp				

Other Information

Coach:

The letters ai, ay, ey, and sometimes ei make the same sound: ay as in day.

Listen to the sound made by the bold letters in the following sentence:

Tod**ay** the men with gr**ey** umbrellas stood in the r**ai**n then went aw**ay**.

Where marked, tell your student the letter combinations (**ay** or **ey**) needed to spell the sounds in each column.

The words gh**o**st, m**o**st, p**o**st and h**o**st are exceptions to the general rule. The **o** carries the long sound.

Do not attempt the same column twice in the same day: one attempt for one tick or dot!

Follow the column guides. Speak clearly.

Day						Day						Day						Day					
Month						Month						Month						Month					
Pro						Spell		ay				Spell		ey				Spell		ay			
hay						*may*						*they*						*dis mayed*					
pay						*dis may*						*grey*						*dis played*					
tray						*dis play*						*con vey*						*spray*					
lay						*say*						*os prey*						*sprayed*					
may						*saying*						*drey*						*starve*					
play						*pay*						*con veying*						*carve*					
say						*paying*						*con veyed*						*starch*					
clay						*stay*						*ghost*						*Monday*					
ey						*staying*						*most*						*due*					
grey						*stray*						*post*						*dues*					
they						*straying*						*host*						*Tuesday*					

Day								
Month								
Pro								
rain								
stain								
pain								
main								
rail								
tail								
wail								
fail								
failure								
stain								
remain								
drain								
Spain								

Day								
Month								
Spell								
stain								
pain								
pains								
train								
fail								
fail ure								
nail								
trail								
they								
con vey								
remain								
drained								
res train								

Day								
Month								
Spell								
com plain								
com plained								
dis dain								
grains								
sail ing								
fail ing								
failed								
trailed								
trailing								
strain ing								
remained								
ob tain								
res trained								

Day						Day						Day					
Month						Month						Month					
Spell						Spell						Spell					
play ful						remain						sprain					
hay						taint						sprained					
drain ing						delay						con tained					
strain ing						delayed						con vey					
painter						or dain						con veyed					
sway ing						or dained						dis play					
stray ing						claim						dis played					
pray ing						claimed						afraid					
play ing						dis claim						plain tiff					
mainland						dis claimed						flailing					
chain						ex claim						hailstone					
trait						avail						bailiff					

Other Information

Coach:

The ghosts that haunt English.

The word **ghost** will play an important role in the spelling of many words throughout The Word Wasp. The letters **gh** are silent in many words and in others they make the sound **f**.

You can tell your student that the letters **gh** in the word **gh**ost **haunt** other words.

In the sentences on the opposite page the letters **gh** are silent. On page 108, remind your student that when the letters **gh** are employed after the letters **ei,** in words like **weigh,** they are also silent.

Another explanation appears in later exercises.

Read and Pronounce

"That is why more civilized people take the **trouble** to **buy First** Class tickets and do not

drag **their** family shopping **through** railway stations," sneered the **woman** in the hat.

If **you** fail to post the mail take a train to the main **station.**

If the train comes off the rails you must hide your **head** and bite your nails.

In the event of a signal failure you must wait until the train stops still then take a bus to

Notting Hill and if that proves to take too long then take a bike to Shepherds Bush.

While the train is in the **station please** refrain from the **temptation** to move your feet

or pick **your** nose. The trains these days are very cramped and expensive.

A tray of clay was hard when baked; much too hard to contemplate being **eaten** by

a hungry vulture. Buttered bones will not tempt them; wings alone have no **meat** on.

The hail failed to stop the mail from being posted and the details **were** sent to the men.

If a dog fails to pick up the trail of the reindeer you may feed it some shrimps and snails.

Show him the way to the wei**gh**ing room where he can check his wei**gh**t and hei**gh**t.

A **gh**ost may have a role to play in the way we spell some **words** today, like wei**gh**t and

frei**gh**t and wei**gh** and slei**gh**.

Day		The ghost is silent	Day		use ey ee	Day		use ei gh	Day		use ai gh
Month			Month			Month			Month		
Pro			Spell			Spell			Spell		
eight			they			weight			container		
weigh			obey			freight			remainder		
weight			drey			vein			memories		
freight			grey			weigh			warrant		
sleigh			weeding			sleigh			wardrobe		
neigh			fleeting			neigh			winched		
straight			Greek			eight			drenched		
watched			agreed			predicted			straight		
warrant			cheer			milked			straighten		
gantry			disobey			resulted			straightened		
instant			career			instant			domineer		
gantries			beer			mem ory			insulted		

Read and Pronounce

Far from the distant empire the **Crown Prince** Henry Jack was considering his exile and

how he might strike back at that distant empire and those he now disdained for taking

all his hard work and then with lies proclaim that the **Crown Prince** was a renegade.

His name was **cursed** and stained.

But the **Crown Prince** was an optimist and some say too laid back to hatch dark plots

and clever plans with which to attack such powerful foes with hate disposed and **whose**

toxic prose he lacked. He **would return** to his homeland and without delay to seek his

friends and those good men, **who** would not the **Prince** betray. They would take the stand;

lend a hand; and remove the unjust stain that sullied all his waking **thoughts** and **caused**

such acute pain. But far, far, far away the Empress mixed a spell: a mixture so **powerful**

her subjects feared the smell. To be tainted with its **odour would** deliver them to **Hellifield**:

a **small village near** Skipton, North **Yorkshire**.

Other Information

Coach:

The letters oy and oi say oy as in boy or oi as in coin.

The rules for the vowel combinations **oy/oi** are a slightly easier version of the rules for **ay/ai**.

Listen to the sounds they make in the following words:

b**oy** depl**oy** c**oi**n m**oi**st.

Demonstrate these sounds on scrap paper before you begin the exercise.

Use the column guides on pages 111-113 to help your student.

Watch out for the word height (Column 1 page 113). It doesn't rhyme with eight or weight but like weight it is a measurement and this is the best place to teach the spelling of the word.

Follow the column guides. Speak clearly.

Day							Day							Day						
Month							Month							Month						
Pro							Spell		oy					Spell		oi				
boy *K W*							*joy*							*join*						
coin *K W*							*boy*							*coin*						
joy Roy							*alloy*							*point*						
soil foil							*toy*							*joint*						
toil join							*decoy*							*annoint*						
boil joint							*annoy*							*spoil*						
annoy spoil							*des troy*							*toilet*						
alloy avoid							*con voy*							*poison*						
ploy anoint							*coy*							*hoist*						
Moira poison							*ploy*							*joist*						
moist hoist							*annoyed*							*moist*						
point joiner							*enjoyed*							*joiner*						

Day						Day						Day						Day					
Month						Month						Month						Month					
Spell	using **ai**					Spell	using **ay**					Spell	using **oi**					Spell	using **oy**				
paint						*tray*						*toil*						*carboy*					
taint						*dis may*						*coin*						*boycott*					
faint						*play*						*soil*						*enjoyed*					
stain						*clay*						*spoiling*						*annoy*					
trailer						*player*						*foiled*						*em ploy*					
main						*play ful*						*loiter*						*joy ful*					
gain						*playing*						*coil*						*des troy*					
pain						*dis play*						*appoint*						*con voy*					
train						*dis played*						*moist*						*dep loy*					
claim						*spray*						*cloister*						*loyal*					
grain						*strayed*						*poisoned*						*royal*					
dainty						*spraying*						*hoisted*						*envoy*					

Day					Day					Day				
Month					Month					Month				
Spell	using **ei**				Spell					Spell				
reindeer					*fix ture*					*extreme*				
vein					*moist ure*					*res tore*				
skein					*plain*					*im plore*				
veil					*complain*					*greetings*				
using the **gh**ost					*explain*					*meetings*				
weight					*explained*					*ad mired*				
freight					*training*					*ex tracted*				
weigh					*raining*					*frozen*				
neigh					*painted*					*sailing*				
sleigh					*painting*					*frail*				
eight					*brains*					*fail ure*				
height					*distaff*					*railings*				

Read and Pronounce

Our words have developed over **many** hundreds of **years** and they come from **many** different lands. The silent '**gh**' in **our words** stems from Saxon England when some words contained a **sound** like a grunt. We no longer employ that **sound** but the letters remain. Like an **old** ghost, they still **haunt our words**. They will **appear** in other **words** which we will **learn** later. As **you work through** The **Word** Wasp **you** will **find** that the **words** in **bold** letters will **slowly disappear because** you will have **learned** to spell and read them.

Cleethorpes is a **place** I **know** where donkeys feel the strain of carrying children, day by day, in sunshine and in rain. They come by bus, they come by car, and sometimes by fast train to put wet bums on donkeys' backs in order to sustain, the misery of donkeys who never do complain. **Katie**, Mike and **Tracy** used to think that spelling was all about memory but **now** they **know** that spelling has rules and they are much happier now they **know** that they are **able to** learn by the same methods that **taught** the **author.**

Do not destroy the daisies that enjoy the sunshine and the shelter of the cloisters.

Read and Pronounce	
To his mum's dismay on holiday	
a greedy boy was playing	
quite unafraid	
with a bucket and spade	
on a sandy shore near Cleethorpes.	
His mum had said, "**Please** listen Fred,	
before you fill your bucket,	
watch the tide by the **seaside**	
it tends to run quite quickly,	
along the bay to where we stay	
it's silent and quite **deadly**."	

Read and Pronounce	
But stolen tarts **were** in Fred's bag	
and nothing could he think of	
but trays of sweets and **ice-cream treats**	
and bon-bons by the gob-full.	
So when the tide swept by his side	
he was swiftly munching.	
He could not run because his tum	
was full from over-lunching.	
Fred's mum was vexed at this upset	
but did expect to see him,	
on the next tide still sat astride,	
a sack of **apple** dumplings.	

Read and Pronounce		
"Take me to your mother,"		
said the spider to the fly.		
"I cannot," said the infant		
"until my wings are dry."		
"Then take me to your brother		
it's quite the same to me;		
I have not had my dinner		
and it's **nearly** ten past three."		
"My brother and mother		
are feeding on a **toad**.		
It failed to see the red light		
and it stepped into the **road**.		
It's been there for eight days now		

Read and Pronounce		
and it's smelling **rather** rank."		
It was at this juncture		
that the spider's spirits sank.		
Then turning white and green again		
was sick into a tank.		
"My wings are now quite dry,"		
said the infant cheerily.		
"If you would like to creep along		
we can meet my family."		
"No! No!" said the spider,		
"It might seem rather rude		
to impose upon your family		
as they eat such tasty food."		

Day				
Month				
Spell				
eight				
freight				
weight				
vein				
scribed				
marker				
starter				
longer				
shorter				
driver				
drover				
decoy				
wanted				

Day				
Month				
Spell				
pusher				
puller				
pushed				
anointed				
painter				
des cribe				
training				
waiter				
strained				
praising				
braised				
braise				
draining				

Day				
Month				
Spell	* past tense rule breakers * * Pro 'sed'			
hover				
lover				
mover				
rover				
loiter				
wanting				
entrails				
lay				
laid *				
pay				
paid *				
say				
said * *				

Day				
Month				
Pro				
dis close				
im pose				
prose				
clothes				
raise				
raised				
praise				
praised				
trainer				
strainer				
spoiled				
joiner				
moisture				

Other Information

Coach:

Adverbs

An adverb describes the action of a verb.

A verb is a '**doing** word' like:

> **running**
>
> **driving**
>
> **smiling**.

The verb can be in the past-tense:

> **ran**
>
> **drove**
>
> **smiled**.

In the following sentences the adverbs are the words formed with **ly** at the end.

The man **was running** (verb) **slowly** (adverb).

The woman **drove** (verb) **quickly** (adverb).

Demonstrate how a word which already ends in **l** like **hopeful** still needs both **l** and **y** to make it into the adverb **hopefully**.

Follow the column guides. Speak clearly.

Day							Day							Day							
Month							Month							Month							
Pro							Spell							Spell		change **y** to **i** and add **ly**					
joyful joyfully							*hormone*							*angry*							
painful painfully							*painful*							*angrily* *							
slow slowly							*loving*							*merry*							
quick quickly							*avoided*							*merrily* *							
mad madly							*bitter*							*noisily* *							
glad gladly							*pay*							*hopeful*							
fresh freshly							*paid*							*hopefully*							
hopeful hopefully							*say*							*thankful*							
tender tenderly							*said*							*thankfully*							
bitter bitterly							*clever*							*happily*							
thankful thankfully							*pointed*							*slowly*							
playful playfully							*playful*							*playfully*							

Read and Pronounce		
Vespula Vulgaris can be a **fearsome beast**.		
Of all our native insects		
It's one that's liked the **least**.		
In June, July, and August		
Wasps struggle to be good.		
By the time October comes around		
The swines are out for blood.		
Open every sandwich.		
Check each can of beer.		
They never fail to find your trail		
They swarm both far and near.		
They love an **ice-cream** cornet		
And jam will soon attract		

Read and Pronounce		
Those black and yellow bandits,		
When the dustbin's been ransacked.		
Father hates them more than most		
In fact he's paranoid;		
Attacking them with dishcloths		
Wet rags and sprays deployed		
But he always seems to miss his foe		
As the kitchen gets destroyed.		
It's **called** a **social** insect		
And one can but wonder why		
Such an anti-**social** animal		
Was given wings to fly.		

Read and Pro nounce

The freight train stopped before the crossing and the man with the flag hailed the man

in the signal box. The other line was blocked by a landslide. Tons of stone, clay and soil

had been moved by the slip and another train was due at **any** time. The man in the

signal box had to move quickly. He ran along the line to the points and pulled the lever.

The rails clanked noisily as the points moved. Seconds later the train came past the points

then, with a sudden unexpected twist, it swung to the left. Tons of steel shifted from side

to side but the train remained on the lines. The man with the flag and the man from

the signal box could not contain their joy at seeing the train miss the landslide.

The landslide was **cleared** the next day.

If the paint dries too quickly; make a complaint to the company that manufactures it.

Take the ointment and anoint your joints and other points where painful lumps and nasty

bumps spoil the joys of life. You **should** be wise and avoid the eyes. Complete the deed

by rubbing the feet with a mixture of linseed oil, garlic and beer. The pain will remain

but the smell will keep away all manner of pests including flies, wasps, and noisy children.

Other Information

Coach:

The u and the w often represent the same sound in English words.

This is particularly true of vowel combinations. Listen to the sound of the letters **ou** and **ow** in the following words:

st**ou**t cl**ow**n tr**ou**t br**ow**n.

In many other words **w** is silent. The **w** in the words in column 3 tells us that the **o** requires its long sound and the **w** is silent. However, regional variations can be tricky.

For the sake of this exercise:

In the exercises on the following pages students will have to make sure that they sound the o and not the w or any part of it.

Day								Day								Day							
Month								Month								Month							
Pro								Pro								Pro							
out *KW*								cow *KW*								show *KW*							
stout								now								low							
about								clown								below							
shout								town								hollow							
round								down								grow							
mound								frown								throw							
sound								gown								mow							
flout								growl								crow							
house								howl								minnow							
louse								allow								window							
mouse								brown								follow							
pouch								crown								shallow							
astound								vowel								thrown							

Other Information

There are words, fortunately very few, which, without a long and protracted discussion of archaisms and old languages, do not lend themselves to easy construction through sounds and rules. A knowledge of the Old Frisian 'wouldest' pronounced 'wowldest' is not going to help my students learn how to spell the word 'would' but the 'ou' combination followed by 'l' allows a small point of reference.

Coach:

This is a normal spelling exercise. Inform your student of the correct combinations before you start each column.

Page 126 contains the words **would, could** and **should**. Demonstrate the spelling on paper. They are related by the **oul** combination and this is the best place to teach them.

Page 126 also contains words like **thought** and **tough**. On scrap paper, show your students how to spell these words by demonstrating the **ou** combinations followed by the **gh**ost **(gh)**. Make sure you refer to the **gh** as "**the ghost**". It is a very useful device!

Page 127: soup, you and youth.

These words contain the **ou** combination but make a different sound. This is the best time to teach these words.

Follow the column guides. Speak clearly.

Day				Day				Day			
Month				Month				Month			
Spell	using ou			Spell	using ow			Spell	using silent w		
spout				now				lower			
trout				cow				slow			
moun tain				down				slower			
pound				allow				throw			
compound				clown				flow			
astound				gown				window			
profound				brown				hollow			
ground				frown				below			
couch				drown				glow			
pouch				brow				glowing			
about				how				throwing			
shouting				crown				showing			

Day						Day						Day						
Month						Month						Month						
Spell						Spell		* silent 'e'				Spell		* Ask your student to use the **ghost** to haunt these words!				
elbow						astonish						could						
diff icult						astound						should						
pros trate						ex pound						would						
placate						throwing						eight *						
proud						flowing						weight *						
shroud						trousers						freight *						
allow						houses						rough *						
com pound						clowns						though *						
towns						house *						thought *						
mound						mouse *						through *						
found						grouse *						tough *						
ground						housing						cough *						

Day				Day				Day			
Month				Month				Month			
Spell	ou			Spell	ow			Spell	ow		
sound				lower				slow			
sounded				lowered				slowed			
found				shower				glow			
founded				showered				glowed			
round				power				row			
rounded				powered				rowed			
mound				crowned				frown			
mounded				powerful				frowned			
count				howler				crown			
flout				drowning				flower			
you				bower				crowned			
youth				cower				crowded			
soup				snowing				towels			

Coach: Make sure you inform your student of the correct letter combinations before he/she starts each column!

Other Information

Coach:

The Return of the Ghost.

This exercise will establish the **ghost** as the mechanism for teaching words which have caused spelling difficulties for many students.

Your student must read every word correctly. Be prepared to offer help with words in bold letters.

Do not attempt the same line twice in the same day: one attempt for one tick or dot!

Read and Pronounce

He thou**gh**t he saw a **gh**ost throu**gh** the window of the old house but he was only **dreaming**.

Our ghosts come from the sounds used by **people** hundreds of years ago. The letters

remain but the sounds have **either** gone or they have been softened. Sometimes our ghosts

exist to fri**gh**ten vowels into saying their loud sound in words such as: s**igh**t and m**igh**t; n**igh**t

and fl**igh**t; br**igh**t and t**igh**t; bl**igh**t and f**igh**t; r**igh**t and l**igh**t. Thou**gh** some **gh**osts are thou**gh**t

to stop some words ending in **u** like thou**gh** and throu**gh.** Other **gh**osts say **f** as in fear in

words like enou**gh**, tou**gh**, rou**gh** and cou**gh**. They **haunt** other words too and we will meet

them soon.

Before we do, there are **smaller gh**osts that come to mind when we look at words like

s**ig**n, des**ig**n and res**ig**n. All our **gh**osts are quite ben**ig**n so let us not their name mal**ig**n.

I do not believe in **gh**osts. The ones I use are tricks that I borrow from history but I do

believe in the power of vowels. These letters are very important.

Other Information

Coach:

The ghost haunts the vowel and makes it say its long /loud sound.

In columns one and two give one tick for each pair of words.

In the Pro Column the red letters highlight the long vowel sound and the ghost is silent.

Do not attempt the same column twice in the same day: one attempt for one tick or dot!

Follow the column guides. Speak clearly.

Day					Day					Day				
Month					Month					Month				
Pro					Spell					Spell				
sight night					*flight sign*					*plight*				
bright plight					*vowels high*					*lighting*				
fight tight					*higher sigh*					*slight*				
light blight					*towels tight*					*slightly*				
fright might					*design low*					*delight*				
slight flight					*slow train*					*sighing*				
right sigh					*light night*					*brighter*				
high mighty					*right bright*					*fighter*				
tighten lighten					*claim sprain*					*eight*				
fighting higher					*pain Spain*					*weight*				
sighing tighter					*rain gain*					*freight*				
design spotlight					*Maidstone*					*height*				

Day					Day					Day					Day				
Month					Month					Month					Month					
Spell	ow				Spell	ou				Spell	oi				Spell	ow				
vow els					out					oil					power					
tow els					stout					soil					flower					
dow els					trout					spoil					trowel					
cowl					clout					avoid					growing					
scowl					flout					avoiding					throwing					
growling					about					joiner					mowing					
cowling					bound					appoint					blowing					
howling					round					coil					glowing					
slowly					sound					boil					bowing					
flow					our					embroil					lowest					
flowing					scour					coins					slowest					
show					flour					groin					snowing					

Day							Day							Day						
Month							Month							Month						
Spell							Spell							Spell						
destroy							they							pure						
highest							convey							picture						
convoy							osprey							structure						
envoy							enough							endure						
destroyer							tough							rupture						
employ							cough							capture						
employer							trough							rapture						
sprightly							though							fracture						
deploy							through							punc ture						
enjoy							thought							demure						
enjoyment							bought							mature						
boycott							nought							posture						

Other Information

Coach:

Homophones.

Your student has been introduced to a number of skills. The next few pages will be devoted to seeing them in action. This will allow for consolidation and the introduction of some homophones: words that sound the same but mean different things.

Do not attempt the same line twice in the same day: one attempt for one tick or dot!

Read and Pronounce

Do not stand on the blue flower which grows in the garden **behind** the flour mill.

If you **pour** oil on your face your pores may become clogged.

Eggs have **their** uses and a baker uses them for baking cakes.

A fowl is a bird like a chicken or a duck but a foul can mean to break the rules by doing something sly or nasty. Refuse to put the refuse in the refuse bin.

A game can be won but one is a number. **Four people** have come for the show.

We can wander along, around, and about or we can wonder at things which amaze and astound us. To wonder is to think; to wander is to move slowly and aimlessly.

If you have been fined then you must pay and you **find** things which have been lost.

It seems as if the **seams** are splitting. He bowled the ball at the bold batsman.

Mind the steps or you might trip. **Coal** was **mined** but now it's ripped and spoils the land.

The **service** duct was very low and the men inside ducked **their heads**.

Tax the rich and put the tacks and nails with the pins and **screws**.

Sail to **France** to buy the wine in the sale or stay at home and pay **too** much tax.

Day				Day				Day				Day			
Month				Month				Month				Month			
Pro				Pro				Spell				Spell			
destroy				you				*over*				*foist*			
highest				youth				*overture*				*catching*			
convoy				soup				*you*				*foiled*			
envoy				through				*youth*				*flinches*			
destroyer				tough				*pure*				*stretches*			
employ				cough				*capture*				*expect*			
employer				trough				*punc ture*				*ex pecting*			
sprightly				enough				*fracture*				*elected*			
deploy				though				*fixture*				*in stinct*			
enjoy				thought				*mixture*				*loiter*			
enjoyed				bought				*extreme*				*loitered*			

Read and Pronounce

Oysters are shellfish that I like to swallow, with pepper and lemon **their** taste is quite

mellow. One must not crunch them; the effect is revolting. Crabs are much better but

require much messing with sticks and picks, they need lots of dressing. Lobsters by far

are the most expensive and with their **claws** they are quite defensive. They can 'take

off' your finger which seems only right if **you're** going to boil them: so impolite! Curried or

fried, shrimps can delight but the sight of **their** skins might give you a fright. Those **eyes**

that look up at you seem small and bright and they remind you that once they saw light.

Take a walk to the 'chippy' and try haddock, deep fried in batter, it may not remind you that

it was **once** swimming free in the **sea** or the lake or the river.

Now **eat** your **tea** and try not to quiver at the thought of fresh fish, just think of liver with

bacon for tea. Does that make you shiver?

Other Information

Coach:

Look at the moon!

Ask your student to listen to the sounds made by the double vowels **(oo)** in the word m**oo**n.

The sound is constant in the first Pro column.

Listen to the sound of the **oo** in the word c**oo**k. The sound is constant in the first Pro column on page 141.

Note: These sounds are subject to many regional variations; particularly in the North. However, this problem arises largely at the pronunciation / reading level only.

The repeated spellings are necessary to make sure that your student can deal with some difficult words.

Follow the column guides. Speak clearly.

Day						Day						Day					
Month						**Month**						**Month**					
Pro						Spell						Spell					
too *KW*						*too*						*spoon*					
soon						*mood*						*eight*					
moon						*food*						*weight*					
doom						*though*						*height*					
gloom						*cool*						*stooping*					
cool						*noon*						*loop*					
fool						*soon*						*loose*					
foolish						*thought*						*noose*					
pool						*bought*						*goose*					
tools						*stool*						*choose*					
loose						*spool*						*brood*					
groom						*doom*						*groomed*					

Day						Day						Day					
Month						Month						Month					
Spell	* The **gh**ost say **f** for fear					Spell						Spell					
tough *						light						bloomer					
rough *						bright						could					
enough *						training						would					
cough *						loose						should					
trough *						goose						moonlight					
through						choose						Blackpool					
foolish						room						foolishly					
cool ant						broom						roof					
troops						boom						proof					
trooper						bloomed						blooming					
trooping						bloom						tooth					
gloomy						loomed						brood					

Day						Day						Day						
Month						Month						Month						
Pro						Spell						Spell						
good *KW*						good						hood						
flood						flood						brother hood						
blood						blood						sister hood						
hood						soot						mother hood						
soot						foot						cooking						
foot						stood						cooked						
rook						took						cooker						
cook						hook						looking						
cooking						wood en						looked						
brook						hooked						crook						
shook						shook						stood						
goods						flooding						understood						

Read and Pronounce

A bull mastiff called Royston was ambling down the Stray,

Rather content to mark his path in the **usual** way,

When along came Homer: a mongrel and a cad,

Who upon seeing Royston was disposed to be quite bad.

Foolishly poor Royston was apt to be unwise:

After burying bones and tasty bits, old pork chops and pies;

He would never fail to mark his trail for a canine cad to find.

A delightful scamp our Homer; an impish plan he chose,

Overtaking Royston by following his nose.

At every tree where Royston's trail hung upon the air;

At every bush and every stump our Homer he was there,

Till at last he came upon a mound down by the Green

Where he dug and scraped so fast his tail could just be seen.

And how it wagged when at last he bagged the Mastiff's store

And lifted his own leg on Royston's pantry door.

Read and Pronounce			Read and Pronounce		
The leech is a parasite;			which regulate the flow		
It has a taste for blood.			of life blood from **their** victims		
It sticks itself to **healthy** things			from which they don't let go.		
and drinks more than it should.			Unless of **course their** greediness		
Leeches are found far and wide			attaches them to one		
not only in the water.			who has a taste for bloodsuckers		
Some are found in bank accounts			that enter his blue pond.		
living off the profits			He will bite them gums and tail		
of others **work**, from which they **shirk**,			until they understand		
like slugs from lime or mortar.			that sucking blood from **healthy** things		
Some of them swim **all** alone,			is rude and impolite		
others swim in **shoals**			and they should drink like others do		
but **all** of them have sucking gums			or **face** the angry pike.		

Other Information

Coach:

The sound made by the letters ea.

The vowel combination **ea** makes three distinctive sounds. Introduce your student to the sounds in the Key Words at the top of each column.

In the word **head** the **a** is silent and the **e** makes its normal sound.

In the word **mean** the vowel **a** gives its power to the letter **e** which then makes its long/loud sound: mean.

In just a few words that break the rules we find the **e** is silent and the **a** makes its long/loud sound:

steak great break

Blue print will denote silent letters.

Day					Day					Day				
Month					Month					Month				
Pro					Pro					Pro				
head *KW*					mean *KW*					steak *KW*				
dead					leaning					great				
instead					clean					greater				
thread					dream					break				
weather					stream					tough				
breakfast					meat					cough				
health					streak					rough				
wealth					bleak					enough				
stealth					leak					host				
peasant					steam					ghost				
feather					dealer					most				
heather					gleaming					post				

Other Information

'Homophones' and their companions 'homonyms' will always cause problems with this particular rule: steak/stake, grate/great, read and pp read, lead and pp led and lead as in pencil or plumbing etc. The pronunciation pages will expose many of them.

Coach:

The next few pages contain normal spelling and pronunciation exercises.

The column guides are important. Make sure your student is aware of the necessary sound before you begin each column.

Listen to the sound of the bold letters in the following words: trea**sure**, mea**sure**. They do not say the word **sure**. The **s** makes a harder sound more like a **z**. Split the words after the **s** which makes the hard sound **z**:

Meas (mezz) + ure   treas (trezz) + ure

The words will be marked by an asterisk (*).

Follow the column guides. Speak clearly.

Day		Day		Day	
Month		Month		Month	
Spell	**ea** as in br**ea**d	Spell	**ea** as in st**ea**m	Spell	**ea** as in st**ea**k
bread		*steam*		*great*	
sweat		*team*		*break*	
dread		*stream*		*steak*	
stealthy		*cream*		*most*	
dreadful		*scream*		*proud*	
weather		*mean*		*cloud*	
feather		*meaning*		*enough*	
heather		*please*		*tough*	
healthy		*ease*		*shout*	
sweating		*disease*		*spout*	
wealthy		*crease*		*trout*	

Day						Day							Day						
Month						Month							Month						
Pro	read both words					Spell	use **ea** to spell						Spell	use **ea** to spell					
steal steel						*measure* *							*treason*						
break brake						*pleasure* *							*reason*						
grate great						*treasure* *							*season*						
steak stake						*stealthy*							*heaped*						
feat feet						*threat*							*meanwhile*						
meat meet						*threaten*							*treat*						
teem team						*dreadful*							*retreat*						
cheep cheap						*headstrong*							*defeat*						
sea see						*headlong*							*feature*						
seam seem						*headlines*							*pleading*						
been bean						*leather*							*bleach*						
peel peal						*thread*							*steam*						

Day						Day						Day					
Month						Month						Month					
Pro	* zure					Spell	* form the v sound					Spell					
ahead						*weave*						*creature*					
close						*wove*						*heater*					
closure *						*leaf*						*bleak*					
deaf						*leaves* *						*jeans*					
deafen						*wife*						*beans*					
deafening						*wives* *						*underneath*					
threat						*self*						*reader*					
threaten						*selves* *						*reading*					
threatening						*wolf*						*leader*					
expose						*wolves* *						*leading*					
exposure *						*beneath*						*weaker*					
instead						*feature*						*dreaming*					

Read and Pronounce

A butcher cleaves meat with a cleaver and a reader reads **books** in the reading room.

Leaves fall from trees and litter the ground. Steel is a metal but to steal is to take

something which **does** not belong to you. You can dream about **ice**-cream or splash in

a stream or you can be mean and keep things for **yourself**.

If you clean your teeth with bleach you may not reach your next **birthday**!

Lean on the lever and steam clean the carpet. Heal the sick and heel the **shoes**.

Everyone would like to be healthy, wealthy and wise. In all kinds of weather, leather

weighs more than feathers. Leather can dry in hot weather. Can you measure the

pleasure of swimming and diving in hot sunny weather? Headlines and deadlines make

a reporter's life difficult. She has read the book which he is reading. He led the team

which she is now leading.

There are **four** seasons and thousands of reasons for reading the **small** print.

Refrain from taking painkillers before you sail because they may fail to sustain your health.

The steak was very tough and the crocodile thought that her teeth were about to break.

You have overcooked this teacher," she growled angrily.

The waiter, an impolite tiger from **Bengal**, picked his **claws** disdainfully:

"You complained yesterday that we had left the watch on the referee from Watford."

"That referee lay so heavily after the meal, I was unable to swim for the rest of the day. I could only float on my back and the pelicans jeered at me all day." replied the crocodile.

"Then there was the accountant from Gateshead," the waiter said dryly, "didn't you say that we must have cooked him in his own books?"

"No that is not quite true. I said that you had cooked him without removing his glasses. Just seeing someone looking up from the plate is enough to put you off meat for life. Why must you insist on cooking them with their heads on anyway?"

"**Chef** thinks that if you remove the head you lose the **flavour**." said the wai**ter.**

"Humans **don't** have much **flavour** unless **they're** wearing aftershave or a **really** strong **deodorant**," huffed the angry reptile.

"Well if you enjoy aftershave or any perfumed seasoning then humans have to be cooked with their heads on," sneered the tiger.

Day										
Month										
Pro										
ear *KW*										
fear										
tear										
near										
Dear										
hear										
hearing										
clear										
year										
rear										
gear										
appear										

Day										
Month										
Pro										
learn *KW*										
learning										
earning										
earnest										
yearn										
pearl										
heard										
yearning										
earth										
dearth										
early										
search										

Day										
Month										
Pro										
teach										
bleach										
peach										
reach										
preach										
preacher										
teacher										
repeat										
defeat										
feature										
creature										
speaker										

Day							
Month							
Spell							
ear							
fear							
tear							
near							
Dear							
hear							
hearing							
clear							
year							
rear							
gear							
fearsome							

Day							
Month							
Spell							
learn							
learning							
earning							
earnest							
yearn							
pearl							
heard							
yearning							
earth							
dearth							
search							
early							

Day							
Month							
Spell							
teach							
bleach							
peach							
reach							
preach							
preacher							
teacher							
repeat							
defeat							
feature							
creature							
weakness							

Other Information

Coach:

The vowel combination oa.

The vowel combination **oa** works just like the mute **e** in as much as the power is moved from right to left. e.g. **pole** = pol e

In the word **coal**, the vowel **o** receives its power from the vowel **a** which remains silent:

co al = **coal**

This is a refreshingly simple rule to spell and pronounce. The power of the vowel moves from the **a** to the **o** and the **o** makes its long sound. Demonstrate the rule on a piece of scrap paper and then follow the spelling columns.

Don't forget: Blue print means that a letter is silent!

Follow the column guides. Speak clearly.

Day		Day		Day	
Month		Month		Month	
Pro		Spell		Spell	
coal		shoal		toast	
white		above		enough	
coast		roar		encroach	
boast		roaming		tough	
ahead		groan		toaster	
which		remove		rough	
foal		moan		poach	
roast		boat		though	
when		stoat		load	
roaming		coast		thought	
while		loan		coach	
why		road		approach	

Day							Day							Day							
Month							Month							Month							
Spell							Spell							Spell							
coast line							bemoan							clean							
here							gloaming							throat							
poaching							moaning							steam							
there							breakfast							moat							
croaking							coaching							roasting							
where							health							approach							
loach							toaster							broad							
read							stealth							dream							
gloat							soap							abroad							
deaf							wealth							mean							
soak							goat							toad							
cloak							cloakroom							oats							

Read and Pronounce

Go to the coast where you might be inclined to spend some time watching ships from abroad unloading **their** cargoes which are loaded on lorries and sent down our roads, while we choke from **their** fumes.

While roasting a goat, our **forbears** once thought of drinking mead and making sport. Don't swallow the dead wasp on the toast and jam when you can eat the live one on the roasted ham.

You may dream of peaches and cream but never **once** think of toadstools. Do not boast about your cooking; the toast will burn while **you** are looking for the butter or the jam. Make a **sandwich** with roast ham; spread it thick with English mustard. Use the powder not the tube but **beware** the tin marked 'custard'. Goad a tiger with a stick if **you** are a lunatic. Encroach upon its quiet repose with a length of oak or rose. Hit it hard upon its nose or stab it hard between its toes. Take a bold and strong approach; jab it **firmly** in the throat but put your name inside each **shoe**; that's all there may be left of **you**! Push a wooden stake into the ground. Fillet steak is expensive and to cattle quite offensive!

Other Information

It isn't always necessary to have a pronunciation exercise before spelling; particularly where the rule is as regular as the one in this exercise.

Coach:

The Word Ending ual.

Like the previous rule: the first vowel, this time the **u**, takes its power from the second vowel **a**, in order that it can say its long sound. However, this time the **a** is stressed only slightly in pronunciation but for spelling the coach must stress the **a**.

Demonstrate the rule on scrap paper and begin the exercise.

Don't forget: Do not attempt a column more than once in the same day!

Follow the column guides. Speak clearly.

Day							Day							Day						
Month							Month							Month						
Spell							Spell							Spell						
casual							residual							light						
seasoned							mutual							sexual						
reasoned							actual							next						
fac tual							per petual							text						
ritual							weight							tex tual						
rough							height							con tex tual						
tough							eight							pleasant						
manual							freight							con tinual						
cough							sensual							peasant						
usual							habit							enough						
dual							hab itual							in div idual						
un usual							eventual							punc tual						

Day						Day						Day					
Month						Month						Month					
Spell						Spell						Spell					
pound						leather						cleaning					
casual						coastline						foaming					
com pound						weather						steaming					
ritually						toasted						groaning					
ex pound						feather						higher					
man ually						roasted						leaning					
ground						heather						fighter					
mutually						boasted						streaming					
sound						boiled						height					
con tin ually						poached						weight					
flounder						reading						freight					
scoun drel						greased						released					

Day						Day						Day					
Month						Month						Month					
Pro	Silent h					Spell						Pro	* **ea** as in h**ea**d				
whether						whether						mean					
which						which						m**ea**nt *					
whelk						whelk						lean					
white						white						l**ea**nt *					
whiff						whiff						empty					
whisk						while						emulate					
while						meanwhile						filthy					
meanwhile						when						tilth					
when						whisk						contract ual					
what						what						pleasure *					
m**a**ny *						many						weather *					
any *						any						individual					

* Ask your student to take note of the vowel **a** in the words 'any' and 'many. These are common words which break the rules.

Day							Day							Day						
Month							Month							Month						
Pro	ai as rain						Pro	ea as in tread						Pro	ea as meal					
constrain							heavy							grease						
against							heavier							leading						
regain							instead							feature						
entertain							bread							creature						
remain							breast							ease						
refrain							dreadful							please						
explain							deadly							disease						
trailer							measure							appease						
retail							treasure							preach						
retailer							breakfast							preacher						
sailor							wealthy							teach						
tailor							healthy							teacher						

Read and Pronounce			Read and Pronounce		
When spores and pollen ride the breeze			As Duncan lay quite fast asleep		
Mr Duncan Rees from Leeds			For the superglue she reached.		
Had a tendency to sneeze.			His snores upon his lips would flutter		
Much to his wife's dismay			"But not for long," she was heard to mutter.		
His teeth would often fly away.			Much has changed for Duncan Rees:		
At great speed and without warning			No longer will his mighty sneeze		
His dentures left his lips one morning;			Propel his **gnashers** through the air.		
Never to be seen until			His teeth redeemed from up the tree		
Mrs Rees from her window sill			Sit grinning from the **mantlepiece**.		
Spied the teeth well out of reach			Now Duncan sleeps in mute repose		
Smiling from a nearby tree.			Emitting through his bunged up nose		
Mrs Rees began to seethe;			Only modest little snores.		
The problem of her husband's teeth			Life for Mrs Rees is sweeter		
Had risen again and could be seen			Much more **wholesome** and completer		
To effect her mood like kerosene			With all the power she can muster		
Unwisely used on barbecues:			With hint of pepper and feather duster		
His **naked** gums had lit her fuse.			She plays upon poor Duncan's fears:		
A terrible plan she now perused.			To have his brains blown through his ears!		

Other Information

Coach:

The sounds air, eir, ear, and are can say air as in fair.

There are many homophones, (words which sound the same and mean different things) involved in this exercise. For instance:

A **pair** of shoes.

A **pear** which can be eaten.

To **pare** with a knife which means to cut or trim.

It is vital, when spelling, that your student understands which form of the letters we are using.

The Pro exercise on page 167 contains an explanation of the possessive pronoun **their**. It doesn't matter if your student doesn't understand it. Be assured: one day he/she will. Once your students have become familiar with the rules and structures of words they will then be receptive to other ideas.

Day					Day					Day				
Month					**Month**					**Month**				
Pro 1					Spell 2	using **air**				Spell 2	using **air**			
fair					*fair*					*despair*				
stairs					*cairn*					*staircase*				
aircraft					*aircraft*					*stairwell*				
fairy					*stairs*					*upstairs*				
dairy					*dairy*					*downstairs*				
flair					*flair*					*fairway*				
hair					*hair*					*impair*				
stairway					*stairway*					*armchair*				
repair					*pair*					*gradual*				
pair					*chair*					*graduate*				
chair					*repair*					*in sin uate*				
armchair					*aired*					*in fat uate*				

A message to coach and student: You've come a long way; keep up the good work!

Day						Day							Day						
Month						Month							Month						
Pro						Spell	**using are**						Spell	**using are**					
fare						*fare*							*declare*						
stare						*flare*							*barely*						
stared						*flared*							*scared*						
flare						*dare*							*nightmare*						
dare						*compare*							*rarely*						
compare						*bare*							*care*						
bare						*hare*							*careful*						
hare						*rare*							Spell	**using ear**					
rare						*spare*							*pear*						
spare						*scare*							*wear*						
scare						*stare*							*bear*						
share						*share*							*tear*						

Read and Pronounce

There are many words which sound the same but they are spelt differently.

We can eat a pear or wear a pair of socks or pare (which means cut) with a knife. We can stare at the stars and **walk** up the stairs. We can run like a hare and lose our hair as we get older.

A hare is a rabbit-like animal that is covered in fine hair which keeps it warm. The letters **eir** can say **air** and if we add a silent **h** to the front which makes **h**eir; it will still sound the same as the word **air**.

We breathe air but an heir is someone who will possess something. Someone who will inherit something is an heir. The word **there** is about a place and it contains the word **here**. The word **their** is about owning something and it contains the word **heir**. There will be a meeting here. Put their hats and coats in the cloakroom. This belongs to them therefore it is theirs.

The word **their** is possessive: It is concerned with ownership. It needs an heir!

Other Information

Coach:

Words ending: er, ar, or, our.

The letters ar / er / or and **our** can make the same sound at the end of a word.
Listen to the following word endings:

coll**ar** doll**ar** bigg**er** small**er** flav**our** col**our**

Demonstrate these endings on scrap paper and then begin the exercise. Be sure to tell your student which ending to use. There are two endings for the third column. The rules are not secrets and they must be revealed.

Follow the column guides. Speak clearly.

Day					Day					Day				
Month					Month					Month				
Spell	using **er**				Spell	using **ar**				Spell	using **our** and **or**			
anger					*beggar*					*vigour*				
bigger					*collar*					*rigour*				
jumper					*dollar*					*colour*				
hamper					*polar*					*savour*				
liver					*molar*					*honour*				
deliver					*solar*					*flavour*				
robber					*pillar*					*tractor*				
banner					*tartar*					*factor*				
flower					*angular*					*sector*				
shower					*sec ular*					*rector*				
thinner					*lunar*					*doctor*				
slender					*reg ular*					*actor*				

Other Information

Coach:

The soft sound of the letter g.

This is an important exercise and once the rule is mastered your student's spelling vocabulary will have been greatly enriched.

Listen to the sound made by the **g** in the following words: **g**in **g**ent en**g**ine **g**yrate.

The **g** is making a sound which we normally associate with the letter **j**.

The rule is: **g** followed by **i, e,** or **y** says **j**.

Follow the column guides. Speak clearly.

Day						Day						Day					
Month						Month						Month					
Pro						Spell						Spell	* stress er				
gate						*agitate*						*gesture*					
gent						*flavour*						*collar*					
agent						*agent*						*gene*					
goad						*gender*						*dollar*					
allergy						*agile*						*genetic*					
agile						*fragile*						*polar*					
agility						*savour*						*gin*					
fragile						*gent*						*molar*					
gender						*favour*						*ginger*					
gymslip						*magic*						*solar*					
ginger						*tragic*						*allergy* *					
danger						*register*						*danger*					

Day						Day						Day						
Month						Month						Month						
Pro						Spell						Spell						
gypsy						*engineer*						*gent*						
allergy						*though*						*logic*						
energy						*tough*						*logical*						
synergy						*strin gent*						*Angela*						
danger						*cough*						*Angelo*						
ranger						*fringe*						*gelignite*						
stranger						*magical*						*ger minate*						
germ						*angelic*						*leth ar gic*						
germinate						*gem*						*large*						
logical						*pun gent*						*digest*						
digit						*gorge*						*charge*						
ingest						*George*						*hinge*						

Read and Pronounce: This passage must be read by students in the normal way. Marking is not required. You may help with words in bold print.

Gradually, a range of strange things began to happen and there was a danger that the dark stranger would find the ginger biscuits which **were** hidden in the pleasure gardens. **Onions** are pungent; they will make you sneeze but not cough in any orthodox way though seeds in the breeze, before they germinate, may terminate their **journey** by sticking in your windpipe. You may ingest them; not digest them. They tend to pass through you. How rude!

Angela and Angelo were both allergic to Gerry. He was often lethargic and would lay on his back eating oranges which were provided, after peeling, by Gemma the gymnast from Brighton.

The regiment was outraged when the regimental goat was eaten by the General. Brigades and platoons were plunged into mayhem when it was heard that he ate a **third** of the animal himself. "**Haul** him before a magistrate," said the irate men. The General remained aloof: "We are going into **battle** tomorrow and the goat may be killed. It would be a pity to waste him." "What about us?" raged the soldiers. "If you die; there will be far too many bodies for the cooks to deal with," returned the General.

Other Information

Coach:

D is for Dam!

You have seen how a **j** sound at the end of a word can be formed by **ge**. However, the **e** does not lose its power to affect the vowel to its left.

e.g. **age**

If we need to stop the power of the **e** reaching the vowel we must build a barrier and dam the flow. We use the letter **d** for that purpose.

e.g. **ba**d**ge**.

The **d** remains silent and the vowel remains short.

Longer words which end with the **idge** (as in **bridge**) sound are usually spelled with the letters **age**.

e.g. vill**age**

In words like ba**r**ge and lu**n**ge, the vowel is already protected from the **e** by the consonant left of the **g**. Don't worry if this seems like a great deal to take on board. The exercises will explain it all.

Day							Day							Day						
Month							Month							Month						
Pro							Pro							Spell	using **d** for **d**am					
sage							village							*lodge*						
fridge							savage							*wedge*						
badge							ravage							*judge*						
page							carnage							*edge*						
lodge							pillage							*sedge*						
budge							manage							*bandage*						
huge							lovage							*bridge*						
grudge							baggage							*Bridget*						
bridge							luggage							*midget*						
oblige							ravage							*gadget*						
gadget							vantage							*fidget*						
sedge							forage							*fudge*						

Day								Day								Day							
Month								Month								Month							
Pro								Spell								Spell							
barge								*forge*								*Stonehenge*							
forge								*lunge*								*revenge*							
lunge								*plunge*								*avenger*							
gorge								*badge*								*bulge*							
sponge								*nudge*								*indulge*							
danger								*fledge*								*gorge*							
divulge								*hinge*								*George*							
indulge								*binge*								*danger*							
large								*charge*								*stranger*							
arrange								*cringe*								*trudge*							
expunge								*avenge*								*budget*							
strange								*grudge*								*arrange*							

Read and Pronounce

In the dark ages, Viking raiders would pillage the villages along the east coast.

Walk up the stairs and stare out of the window.

Cut the cloth with a pair of **scissors** and savour a pear before its flavour becomes impaired or too ripe to eat.

A gradual approach to spelling, using rules and structure, is better than trying to **guess** or remember from a long list which contain lots of different types of words.

A flare is a rocket that lightens the sky and flair is a talent or skill.

A manual worker has just as much right to use a pen as a teacher or a doctor.

Individual pies can make your **eyes** water if they are covered in pepper or chillies.

The loudest account of events is usually the least factual.

Beware of the jackals that gather like vultures. They steal the meat from the hand of their brother.

George was a corporal in the Signals and his brother was a lance corporal in the Royal Engineers.

Read and Pronounce

The bear could no longer endure the **cold**. She felt quite bare in the cold weather. Bruno, her estranged husband, didn't know whether to hide from the weather **either**. He was still on good terms with his former partner and he had bumped into her by accident as they **were** raiding the dustbins outside the local hunting lodge. "What a very poor diet these hunters have!" said Angela. "They come here hunting bears so they can mount heads on a wall, our heads, they eat this garbage: **pizza**, burgers, and all the usual junk food. I mean there are deer, rabbits, and pheasants out there! Why pick on us? They don't even like bear meat!"

"Which reminds me!" said Bruno, "Where are they?"

"Sleeping it off! They haven't seen a bear all day. I know! I followed them. They left a trail of empty beer cans right through the forest."

"Did they drink it all?" enquired Bruno.

"No! They left two cases by the river: they were too drunk to carry them."

"Tell you what Angela! I've been thinking. I'm ready to hibernate. In fact I've just about finished digging my new pad just above the snow-line. How about you and me having a little meal for two before we get our heads down for the winter?"

"What! Just you and me? Are you sure? Well maybe! But we had better not argue."

"Well I thought if you haven't dug yours yet you might think about staying for a while."

"You always were an old romantic. Go get the beer; I'll bring the **pizza**."

Read and Pronounce

Her Royal Highness, the Empress, has been troubled by double **vision** for **many** years.
After a severe bout of seemingly unprovoked anger she stormed out of the room, took the
wrong alternative and fell, headlong, down the **wrong** staircase. Her subjects took their
leave **rather** quickly; leaving her to curse and swear at her own misfortune. There was
little choice. Their fate would have been terrible had they been present at her loss of
dignity. There was little choice but to flee while their heads remained on their **shoulders**.
Any remaining thoughts that she might cool her temper with ice-cream, a delicacy she
was very fond of, soon disappeared. When asked to savour a new flavour some hours
later she replied with vigour that any peasant known to have been present at the time been
present at the time of her accident would be sent to the 'Tower', rolled in flour, toasted and
roasted, their heads put on stakes, their other bits minced and despatched to the fringes as
parcels of meat to feed the dogs and wild beasts that feast on pheasants and sometimes
peasants who stray from their homes to tend to their sheep.

Coach: The word **was** applies to one person or thing. The word **were** applies to two or more persons or things. Allow your student to read the sentences in the first column and mark it in the usual way.
The second column invites your student to read all the sentences but where w_____ occurs your student must write either **was** or **were** - on scrap paper not in the book! It is not enough for your student to say the word. He/she must write the word in every case.

			The walls w_____ bare and stripped of paint.		
The judge **was** sleeping on his bench.			The cat w_____ feeling rather faint.		
The defendants **were** swearing oaths in French.			She sank her teeth in George's bottom.		
Not many people **were** signing the pledge.			I think he will ride cats no more.		
The General **was** inspecting the men.			One team w_____ playing.		
The men **were** not expecting the general.			The players w_____ playing.		
The clouds **were** gathering in the sky.			The village smithy w_____ taking snuff.		
The sun **was** shining in my **eyes**.			The flavour of the sweet w_____ horrid.		
The wasps **were** swarming on the jam.			The women on the ridge w_____ very angry.		
His mother **was** dancing upon the stairs.			The refugees w_____ tired and hungry.		
His father **was** watching in **disbelief.**			Disease w_____ spreading through the village.		
George **was** sitting on the cat.			Butter mountains w_____ melting in the hot sun.		
The cat **was** looking quite annoyed.			**You were very unpleasant!**		
The bears **were** fishing in the pond.			**The word you breaks the rule.**		
Two brown bears **were** eating pears.			**It can apply to one or both of you.**		
Where **were** their clothes?					

Coach: 1 Ask your student to read the bold words in the spelling   column and then the corresponding phrase. Do not mark!
2 Work down the spelling column in the normal way demonstrating the appropriate words by reading the phrases opposite each word.   Mark the grid. Two consecutive ticks are needed.

Pro once only

Spell	Read the line					arrange				
pair	a pair of shoes					danger				
stairs	that one climbs to bed					stranger				
bear	an animal that lives in the forest					strange				
pear	a fruit that we eat					range				
wear	as in clothes that we wear					grange				
where	a place where we might live					hinge hinged				
hair	that grows on your head					cringe cringed				
heir	someone who will own something					forge forged				
pare	to cut with a knife					large enlarged				
bare	to be without clothes					lunge lunged				
stare	to look intensely					plunge plunged				
their	something that is owned by people					charge charged				
there	a place where something exists or happens					stage staged				

Other Information

Coach:

The Soft C Rule.

So that's what K is for!

In the basic sounds we learned that both **c** and **k** make the same sound in words like **cat** and **kipper**. However, if we use a **c** before an **i**, **e**, or **y**; the sound changes to an **s**. Listen to the sound in the following words:

 cent, **c**ivil, **c**ymbal, **c**ity.

In English words, where we need a **c** sound before the letters **e** **i** or **y** we have to use a **k**.

We call this use of the letter **c**: **The Soft C Rule**.

S at the end of a word can often say **z** but **ce** always makes the soft sound of **s**.

Follow the column guides. Speak clearly.

Day					Day					Day		*split the sounds			Day			
Month					Month					Month					Month			
Pro					Pro					Spell					Spell			
cell					dance					*lance*					*pacify*			
kelp					one					*chance*					*civilize*			
cent					once					*France*					*concentric*			
price					glance					*glance*					*bounce*			
race					romance					*dance*					*ounce*			
chance					produce					*village*					*flounce*			
Kipper					fence					*romance*					*trounce*			
finance					ounce					*celery*					*announce*			
cellar					bounce					*celebrate*					*advice*			
cynic					trounce					*civic*					*advise*			
ex cept					flounce					*ex cept **					*slice*			
ex cite					cider					*ex cite **					*placid*			

Other Information

Coach:

Double C.

Many words use a double **c (cc)** to produce a **c** sound followed by a **s sound**. Listen to the following word:

a**cc**ent.

It is the **soft c** rule once more. It just seems complicated by having double letters.

If the letters **cc** are followed by an **e** or **i** then the first letter says **c** as in **c**ar and the second **c** forms the **soft c** sound.

In the Pro column the **c** highlighted in red must be pronounced as a **s**.

Follow the column guides. Speak clearly.

Day						Day						Day					
Month						Month						Month					
Pro						Spell		soft c				Spell		a mixture			
ac cept						*ac cept*						*accord*					
accord						*ac cede*						*occur*					
ac cent						*ac cident*						*account*					
accolade						*oc cident*						*accumulate*					
ac cede						*ac celerate*						*accomplish*					
accuse						*ec centric*						*occlude*					
ac cident						*ac cent*						*occupy*					
occur						*ac cess*						*succulent*					
ec centric						*suc cess*						*suc cessive*					
hiccup						*suc ceed*						*accuse*					
policy						*oc ciput*						*recite*					
vac cinate						*suc cinct*						*ac cip itral*					

Day		Day		Day	
Month		Month		Month	
Spell	* k before e and i	Spell		Spell	
kelp *		price		trace	
fence		priced		specific	
trance		advice		peace	
chance		race		atrocity	
mince		embrace		electricity	
kitten *		lace		spliced	
romance		place		recite	
France		placid		nice	
advance		pacific		fallacy	
distance		pacify		vicinity	
finance		specify		censure	
convince		lance		quince	

Read and Pronounce

Give notice to the service of the menace which stems from the palace of the Empress

where a poisoned chalice will be offered with malice to those who challenge the decrees

and edicts of the Royal Office. It has long been the policy in that **region** to exile or send

to the **foreign legion** all those who offend against her **religion**.

A decimal point on a bank balance can make the difference between joy and misery.

Acceptance of advice before an advance may not lead to the chance of romance with the

woman from France. Do not think twice but break the ice and treat the lice or you will pay

the price with an itchy scalp. You will have success with the correct shampoo. Soap alone

will not do and consider not a tube of glue. In the precinct, a distinct smell of tar and gin

floats in and out of cellars grim where heads are shaved and bodies waxed and fleas and mice

live free from tax. The recent rains have washed the plains and clouds of flies have

advanced within reach of the crowded beach. Are eccentric people more accident prone?

Convince the man from the palace that the **women** in the province are advancing quickly.

Other Information

Coach:

More Soft C.

This is a pronunciation and spelling exercise. The **our** endings have been grouped together.

Remind your student once more, if necessary, that **bought, though** and **through** need to be haunted!

Note: In the words in the first column ending **ice** the vowel **i** takes its short sound.

Words in column three ending **ace** must have the **a** stressed. Ask your student for the proper pronunciation immediately after he/she has spelled the word concerned.

Day							Day							Day						
Month							Month							Month						
Pro							Spell							Spell						
malice							*colour*							*malice*						
notice							*flavour*							*notice*						
Alice							*savour*							*novice*						
novice							*honour*							*Alice*						
chalice							*brown*							*chalice*						
coppice							*clown*							*concern*						
cornice							*frown*							*cornice*						
lattice							*down*							*office*						
office							*bought*							*menace*						
menace							*thought*							*palace*						
palace							*through*							*lattice*						
cystic							*cystic*							*farce*						

Other Information

Just for the record: guard and guardian are variant forms of the Old Northern French and Anglo Norman word 'wardein' (warder) which is a variant of the Old French word 'g(u)arden' (guardian).

I am the gu**a**rd and this is my shield!

Coach:

I am the gu**ard!**

The letter **u** can protect the **g** from the power of the vowels **e** and **i**. If we want the letter **g** to make its normal sound before the letters **e** and **i** we can place a shield between the letter **g** and the vowel. It remains silent but protects the letter.

The sound made by the following letters: **gest** is the same as the word **jest**. But I am expecting **guests** for dinner!

As the **u** is a guard we find it in its own name: g**u**ard. A g**u**arantee is a g**u**ard too!

The rule for soft **c** is the same: cir**cu**it - bis**cu**it. The **u** allows the **c** in each word to say **c** as in **car**.

Day						
Month						
Pro						
guide						
guest						
guard						
garden						
guarantee						
biscuit						
circuit						
guess						
guitar						
guilt						
guilty						
vogue						

Day						
Month						
Spell						
gender						
gentry						
damaged						
managed						
outraged						
caged						
savaged						
ravaged						
cent igrade						
pacify						
pacified						
decimate						

Day						
Month						
Spell						
guide						
vogue						
guard						
garden						
guar antee						
biscuit						
circuit						
guitar						
gastric						
guilt						
specify						
guess						

Day									Day									Day								
Month									Month									Month								
Spell									Spell									Spell								
agile									congested									slight								
fragile									judgement									ginger								
guess									Egypt									face								
ledger									gypsy									facet								
thought									gyrate									facile								
bought									passage									guitar								
guide									message									glance								
guile									village									rogue								
beguile									eight									disguise								
algebra									weight									notice								
general									height									guard								
league									plague									gerund								

Read and Pronounce

Words that have entered our **language** from the tribes of the North German plain do not follow

the rule for 'Soft G': give, begin, forget, burger, forgive, get. There is a debate about the word

'gypsy'. Some people think that it should be spelled with an '**i**': **gi**psy. Other people make the point

that travelling people originally came from Egypt and the word 'gypsy' came from a shorthand

form of the word '**Egyptian**'.

In some words 'u' can make the same sound as 'w'. This happens with words containing 'qu'.

The 'q' makes the sound of a 'c' and 'u' makes the sound of a 'w'. Listen to the sound made by 'qu'

in the word '**qu**ick'. Then listen to the sound made by the letter 'u' in the words 'peng**u**in', 'pers**u**ade'

'lang**u**age', 'ling**u**ist', and 'ling**u**istic'. We will meet these words again.

Now you have reached this stage of the book you may have noticed that your reading skills have

improved with your spelling skills. Some people think that spelling and reading are separate

skills. What do you think? **I think you are getting the message!**

Other Information

Coach:

Le Endings.

Listen to the sound of the letters **le** at the end of the word **cattle**.

Demonstrate the **le** ending on scrap paper and start the exercise. The first and second columns require twin consonants, be sure to tell your student. **Mangle and angle already have two consonants before the le.**

Note:

The last four words in column 3 (double, trouble, couple, touch) have to be taught as exceptions to the rules. When pronouncing the words sound the **ou** as in **cloud.** Then ask your student to give you the proper pronunciation. He/she may fail the first time but you will be unlucky if it happens twice.

Follow the column guides. Speak clearly.

Day		Day		Day	
Month		Month		Month	
Spell		Spell		Spell	*say ou as in cloud
settle		cobble		gentle	
kettle		hobble		angle	
nettle		rubble		dangle	
fettle		paddle		candle	
muddle		middle		handle	
puddle		bottle		ankle	
saddle		shuttle		single	
bubble		shuffle		mingle	
stubble		riddle		double *	
throttle		hassle		trouble *	
quibble		apple		couple *	
mangle		spangle		touch *	

Day		Day		Day	
Month		Month		Month	
Pro	without soft g	Spell		Spell	soft c
begin		*begin*		*farce*	
clanger		*battle*		*farcical*	
banger		*anger*		*entice*	
get		*cattle*		*device*	
give		*girdle*		*vicinity*	
given		*raffle*		*cinder*	
forgive		*given*		*force*	
forget		*uncle*		*brace*	
anger		*banger*		*ounce*	
girl		*crumple*		*bounce*	
girdle		*longer*		*trounce*	
gift		*bungle*		*cynical*	

Read & Pro

The **trouble** with '**double**' and '**couple**' is the vowel combination '**ou**'. To some people in the North it might seem to have a surplus 'o'. However, some people in the South might think that the 'u' was unnecessary. It's all quite a muddle. Play a fiddle; solve a riddle; saddle a horse; step over a puddle; stay free and single; marry and mingle. Coins jingle; nerves jangle; families **squabble**; dust settles; kettles boil; nettles sting; skittles fall; Tarzan swings through the jungle; dyslexics' spellings are in a muddle; but the Word Wasp helps them with their struggle. Thread a needle; hold a handle; try to avoid the deepest puddles; or you may find that your ankles are soaking wet and you must dangle them above the fire: (in the absence of a mangle). Percy and Cecil were **friends** of both **Cynthia** and Gerry who had just moved to the **centre** of the city. High above the ridge and beyond the hedge; far from the village and under a ledge; a badger took a lodger into her lodge and little did the council **know:** she had ten more lodgers down below! You must announce that a bouncing baby girl has been born and she weighs seven pounds and eight ounces.

It is possible; indeed probable, that a vegetable might not be edible before cooking.

Other Information

Coach:

The letters au and aw, say or as in for.
Ask your student to listen to the following
sounds:

> **au** in the word P**au**l.
> **aw** in the word l**aw**.

Don't forget to stress both parts of the word
because in the spelling columns
be and **cause:** not **coz!**

Your student must hear the **au** saying **or**.

Day				Day				Day				Day			
Month				Month				Month				Month			
Pro	au			Pro	au			Pro	aw			Pro	aw		
Paul				cause				saw				jigsaw			
maul				because				sawn				withdraw			
August				pause				paw				drawn			
launch				audit				outlaw				crawl			
fraud				gaudy				draw				crawling			
taunt				laundry				claw				sprawl			
gaunt				flaunt				fawn				dawn			
saunter				haul				straw				drawing			
daunted				haulage				jackdaw				trawler			
haunt				trauma				lawn				hawk			
haunted				staunch				pawn				yawning			
austere				defraud				sawdust				flawed			

Day						Day						Day					
Month						Month						Month					
Spell	au					Spell	au					Spell	au				
Paul						gaunt						flaunt					
kettle						little						ankle					
maul						saunter						staunch					
strangle						shuttle						gargle					
August						daunted						haulage					
autonomy						straddle						topple					
launched						haunt						nautical					
tan gent						wiggle						laundry					
fraud						haunted						noon					
middle						angle						noodle					
taunt						gaudy						pause					
haunches						audit						applaud					

Day						Day						Day					
Month						Month						Month					
Spell	aw					Spell	aw					Spell	aw				
cause						outlaw						sprawl					
because						weight						double					
dawn						straw						sprawling					
trounce						freight						guard					
prawn						trawler						brawl					
evident						height						guiding					
lawn						withdrawn						crawling					
evidence						trouble						couch					
spawn						yawn						awning					
trance						couple						ouch!					
drawn						yawning						touch					
awfully						lawfully						draw					

Read & Pronounce

The image of the Common Wasp, Vespula Vulgaris, is generally bad. They are at their worst in late **Autumn**. When the breeding season is over, swarms of redundant males gather around dustbins or anywhere that can supply an easily available **source** of food. It's as if they are having one last binge before they die. However, there is another side to these insects. They carry a sting which is the main cause of concern and fear but in many ways they are **beneficial** insects with a highly developed social structure. The Queen wasps alone survive the winter. Emerging in late spring, they begin to search for a nest site. These are the huge wasps we see in our houses in late May. Once a site has been found construction begins at a pace. The nest is made from paper or dried grass: anything which can be chewed into a pulp is cemented together to form a nest. The Queen has carried a small packet of sperm throughout her hibernation which she uses to fertilize her first eggs. The young are born as grubs; highly prized amongst anglers as fishing bait. These grubs will develop into infertile female workers. They will tend to the further construction of the nest and the feeding of the young. Then, in mid-autumn, for reasons yet to be explained, the eggs laid develop into fertile males and females. These wasps mate and the females or Queens will hibernate and the cycle begins again. Left to themselves wasps are not usually aggressive. However, hot weather and overcrowded nests

Read & Pronounce

can lead to wasps developing an attitude problem. Wasps have mood swings!

Unlike the bee, the wasp's sting does not have a barb and it can use it several times. The spike

is a type of ovipositor (egg-laying tube) which has been modified to facilitate the wasp's defensive

or offensive needs. The **notion** that a wasp's sting is alkaline is false. The sting is **neutral**, (pH 6.8)

so smothering the effected **area** with **either** vinegar or bicarbonate of soda is not much use.

Use a **special** bite cream and apply ice to reduce the swelling.

The full name of the the Common Wasp is Vespula or Paravespula Vulgaris. It belongs to the

family (Hy/men/op/tera) Hymenoptera which also includes other wasps such as the German wasp:

Paravespula Germanicus and the Hornet:Vespa Crabro. Ants also belong to the same family.

Some people attempt to accommodate wasps by upholding their role as pest controllers. They

feed their developing young on a whole range of (in/ver/te/brates) invertebrates. Invertebrate means

without bone structure. Wasps, like bees, visit flowers and therefore distribute pollen and assist in

pollination. Unfortunately, their bad **behaviour** is predominant in the minds of many whose

paranoia will only be relieved by swatting them.

That was hard going but are you not amazed at your progress? You can't swat The Word Wasp!

Other Information

Coach:

In most common words ending in the vowel **o** the **o** takes its long/loud sound:

Listen to the **o** in carg**o**.   Extending these words with an **s** sound requires the letters **es** : cargo**es**.

The word **do** ends in the letter **o** and therefore it requires **es** to form **does.**

Ask your student to work through the Pro column and mark in the usual way.

Day									
Month									
Pro									
embargo									
embargoes									
cargo									
cargoes									
tomato									
tomatoes									
potato									
potatoes									
undergo									
undergoes									
hero									
heroes									

Day									
Month									
Pro									
go									
goes									
going									
do									
does									
doing									
zero									
zeroes									
so									
also									
always									
many									

Day									
Month									
Spell									
cargo cargoes									
go goes going									
do does doing									
so also always									
potato potatoes									
tomato tomatoes									
any many anyway									
pay paying paid									
lay laying laid									
say saying said									
colour flavour									
savour vigour									

Other Information

Coach:

The letter U can say W.

Listen to the sound of the letter **u** in the word peng**u**in.

Write the following words **penguin** and **pengwin** to demonstrate the action of the **u**. **Penguin** is the proper spelling but both sound alike.

Demonstrate the sound on scrap paper and then start the Pro column.

Follow the column guides. Speak clearly.

Day							Day							Day						
Month							Month							Month						
Pro							Spell	sound the 'i' in ible						Spell	'u' can say 'w'					
penguin							*possible*							*pen guin*						
anguish							*sensible*							*an guish*						
extinguish							*edible*							*extin guish*						
vanquish							*visible*							*van quish*						
persuade							*multiple*							*per suade*						
banquet							*credible*							*ban quet*						
languish							*edible*							*lan guish*						
language							*responsible*							*lan guid*						
linguist							*couple*							*lan guage*						
linguistic							*double*							*lin guist*						
sanguine							*trouble*							*lin guistic*						
frequent							*touch*							*frequent*						

Day							Day							Day						
Month							Month							Month						
Spell	aw/oi/soft c						Spell	au/oi & the ghost						Pro						
flawless							audit							weather						
voice							ointment							feather						
awful							fauna							leather						
rejoice							appointed							feeble						
lawful							staunched							needle						
spoiled							loiter							beetle						
scrawl							vaunted							seedling						
invoice							loitered							posture						
brawl							taunted							flavoured						
avoided							caught							coloured						
withdraw							taught							honoured						
choice							distraught							savoured						

Read and Pronounce - Watch for the ghost!

Claude was hauled before the magistrate for defrauding Maude and Audrey of their haul

of paintings. These had already been procured from Maureen who had stored them since

August. The evidence was mounting but the guests at the wedding were friends of Claude.

This had caused much anguish at the banquet where the language was said to be so

naughty that the haughty Mr Gaunt was caught off guard. He was **heard** to observe

"that it was about time someone said goodnight to Rosemary Rudeness and good morning to

Margaret Manners".

The local lawn tennis club needed a new awning, but not having enough funds, members

of the committee decided to carry out a dawn raid on a rival club. Still yawning they

launched their assault by vaulting the perimeter fence. Tipped off by the disgruntled

Mrs Saunders, who had been dropped from the mixed doubles team, their rivals were

waiting and served volley after volley of stinging balls at the raiders as they crawled back over

the fence. The slaughter was terrible and the **bruises** were horrible and even the President's

daughter was caught by a **ferocious** thump to her rump.

Other Information

Pro columns for this exercise are not always helpful. Some students cannot make the appropriate 'ew' sound as in 'news' without a great deal of coaching. Adults can be particularly self- conscious when attempting these sounds.

Coach:

The Sound of ew.

Listen to the sound made by the letters **ew** in the word st**ew**. They sound like the word **you**.

Listen to the sound made by the same letters in the word fl**ew**. They sound like the word **who**.

Demonstrate the rule on scrap paper then start the spelling column.

You must remember to pronounce the **au** vowel combination as **or**, in the words f**au**lt, v**au**lt, ass**au**lt. The words must be corrected in the pronunciation exercises.

L**au**ghter and dr**au**ght are odd words which follow the same structure but not the sound as d**au**ghter and sl**au**ghter. Inform your students of this before you ask them to spell the words.

Do not harass your student if he/she cannot produce the right pronunciation of the letters **ew**.

Follow the column guides. Speak clearly.

Day							Day							Day						
Month							Month							Month						
Spell							Spell							Spell						
pew							withdrew							account						
drew							Lewis							mounted						
pewter							brewed							fault						
hew							threw							vault						
grew							brewery							assault						
hewn							Lewisham							caught						
stew							crew							taught						
strewn							spew							daughter						
few							new							slaughter						
dew							spewing							laugh						
blew							stewed							laughed						
brew							Andrew							laughter						

COACH AND STUDENT: Read Pronounce and above all take note!

This exercise is designed to make sure that both coach and student are **familiar** with the needs of the exercise on the opposite page. The repetitive nature of many of the exercises makes it too easy to miss out important pieces of **information**.

The **instructions** for the exercises on the opposite page have now become part of the **pronunciation** exercise; insuring that both coach and student have the best possible **preparation** for the tasks ahead which are much easier than you might think.

We make the sound normally **associated** with the letters **sh** in many words but most of them are not spelled using **sh**. There is a very tight code which you will learn by following the **instructions** over the next few pages.

Exercise A. The blue example **section** shows the letters that form the **sh** sound. A tick has been placed under the letters that combine to form the sound. **Check now!** In the white **section** the student is invited to tick the boxes under the **sh** sound. The **(3)** indicates that there are three elements saying **sh** to be ticked. **Do this now!**

Exercise B. The letters **ti** followed by a vowel, usually an **o** are the most common way to form the **sh** sound: **ti** plus a vowel says **sh**: e.g. **mention, patient, nation**. In almost every word formed this way the vowel acts as a pointer to the **ti** and declares that **ti** says **sh**. The vowel usually stays silent. Look for **ti** followed by a vowel; mark it and say **sh**.

Exercise A

t	u	j	n	p	s	h	o	l	f	t	i	m	s	h	a	d	t	i	v	s	h	o	n	g	l
					/	/							/	/						/	/				

Example Above

s	h	o	l	k	i	t	h	s	o	s	h	i	l	d	r	s	h	f	j	o	s	s	o	h	p

find and tick the sh sounds   (3)

Exercise B

t	i	p	u	m	t	i	o	l	p	t	i	e	k	p	t	i	o	m	l	t	i	s	t	i	o
				/	/	◄				/	/	◄			/	/	◄						/	/	◄

Example Above

p	t	t	i	o	l	t	i	a	t	i	o	t	i	g	t	i	o	k	t	i	e	n	t	i	m

t i followed by a vowel says sh - Find and tick the sh sounds   (5)

Other Information

Coach:

The Common Spelling of 'tion'.

Listen to the sound made by the bold letters in the word men**tion**.

You will hear that sound in many words and there are many ways to spell that sound but by far the most common is when the vowel **o** points to the **ti** and indicates that the letters are saying **sh**.

tion = shon   The **o** is unstressed (sh'n).

In the Pro column, all the sounds and words in each line must be pronounced to gain the tick.

Follow the column guides. Speak clearly.

Day						Day						Day					
Month						Month						Month					
Pro						Spell						Spell					
tion ation nation						*nation*						*selection*					
tion otion notion						*station*						*production*					
lotion potion action						*notion*						*infection*					
section fraction						*motion*						*instruction*					
suction traction						*section*						*construction*					
devotion emotion						*elation*						*solution*					
condition infection						*lotion*						*pollution*					
selection solution						*action*						*rev olution*					
promotion elation						*fraction*						*addiction*					
direction induction						*edition*						*reduction*					
partition election						*condition*						*introduction*					
collection pollution						*friction*						*contraction*					

Read Pronounce and above all take note!

Most **tions** are formed with a **t** but some are formed with an **s** like pen**s**ion and ten**s**ion

but there is another sound which is almost always spelled with a **s** and that is the sound

made in the following words: vi**si**on and fu**si**on. It is not a **sh** sound at all! It is a French

sound. Listen to the bold part of the following words: vi**sion**, colli**sion**. Say that sound **now!**

The Word Wasp calls that sound **hard sh.**

When you hear that sound you will know that it is spelled using **si** followed by a vowel.

You will soon be able to spell words like notion, lotion, tension, pension, compression and

compassion, as well as vision, invasion, Asian, decision and caution.

The one exception known by the author is the word equation.

Look at the examples on the opposite page and complete the exercises beneath them.

s	i	o	n	p	s	o	i	s	p	s	i	o	f	g	i	l	s	i	o	s	i	a	j	s	t
/	/	◄						/	/	◄						/	/	◄	/	/	◄				

Example Above

s	i	a	l	d	s	i	o	l	p	h	s	i	a	p	s	i	m	n	s	o	i	p	s	o	i

si followed by a vowel can say hard sh as in vision or Asia - tick and say the sound.
3 only

s	a	i	l	d	s	i	o	l	a	s	i	o	t	p	s	i	o	n	s	o	i	p	s	i	o

4 only

t	o	i	s	s	o	i	t	i	o	n	s	o	i	t	s	i	o	n	t	s	i	o	i	s	l

A mixture of ti and si followed by a vowel - find and mark.
3 only

Other Information

Coach:

The sound of sion as in vision.

Both words in the Pro columns must be read correctly to earn a tick.

Follow the column guides. Speak clearly.

Day						Day						Day					
Month						Month						Month					
Pro						Spell						Spell					
vision television						*vision*						*precision*					
invade invasion						*provision*						*conclude*					
explode explosion						*invasion*						*conclusion*					
incision decision						*profusion*						*version*					
divide division						*explosion*						*conversion*					
include inclusion						*inclusion*						*verge*					
exclude exclusion						*corrosion*						*verger*					
provide provision						*exclusion*						*merge*					
fuse fusion						*decision*						*merger*					
confuse confusion						*confusion*						*occasion*					
deride derision						*incision*						*ad hesion*					
revise revision						*revision*						*ex cision*					

Other Information

Coach:

More spelling with tion and sion.

The first two columns contain words using **soft sion** which sounds the same as **tion** as in **mention**. The last column contains words using **hard sion** as in **vision**.

Follow the column guides. Speak clearly.

Day						Day						Day					
Month						Month						Month					
Spell						Spell						Spell	hard sion				
compress						tension						invasion					
compression						pension						confusion					
express						suspension						illusion					
expression						oppress						decision					
passion						oppression						vision					
compassion						mission						television					
depress						commission						precision					
depression						permission						collision					
impress						mansion						profuse					
impression						expansion						profusion					
profess						expel						ex clusion					
profession						expulsion						corrosion					

Other Information

Coach:

The spelling cian refers to a person.

Listen to the sound made by the letters **cian** at the end of the word **optician.**

It make the same sound as **tion** ('**sh'n**').

This is an example of **person cian**. The letters **ci** followed by a vowel say **sh.** Therefore **ci** followed by **a** and then **n (c i a n)** means that we are dealing with a person:

> **politician**
>
> **technician**
>
> **electrician**
>
> **magician**

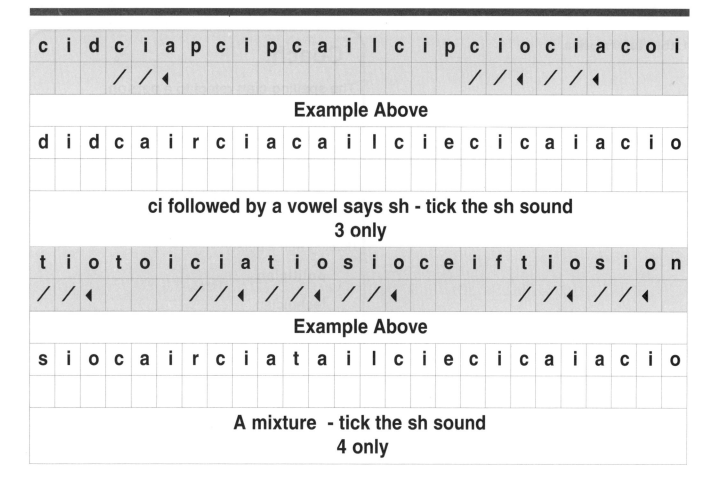

c	i	d	c	i	a	p	c	i	p	c	a	i	l	c	i	p	c	i	o	c	i	a	c	o	i
			/	/	◄										/	/	◄	/	/	◄					

Example Above

d	i	d	c	a	i	r	c	i	a	c	a	i	l	c	i	e	c	i	c	a	i	a	c	i	o

ci followed by a vowel says sh - tick the sh sound
3 only

t	i	o	t	o	i	c	i	a	t	i	o	s	i	o	c	e	i	f	t	i	o	s	i	o	n
/	/	◄			/	/	◄	/	/	◄	/	/	◄						/	/	◄	/	/	◄	

Example Above

s	i	o	c	a	i	r	c	i	a	t	a	i	l	c	i	e	c	i	c	a	i	a	c	i	o

A mixture - tick the sh sound
4 only

Other Information

Coach:

Words containing cian and cious.

These words may look difficult but the rules make them much easier to spell.

Advise your student on the type of word ending needed.

Note: **CIOUS**

ci is followed by the pointer: c i ◀ us

The pointer is **o**:   c i + o = sh

The pointer (**o**) is silent: c i o = sh

The letters **us** says **us** as in m**us**t:

cio + us = shus

Follow the column guides. Speak clearly.

Day						Day						Day					
Month						Month						Month					
Pro	* X = c s					Spell	**person cian**					Spell					
cian ician						*optician*						*precious*					
magician						*magician*						*gracious*					
optician						*politician*						*spacious*					
electrician						*electrician*						*audacious*					
logician						*logician*						*mendacious*					
politician						*clinician*						*vivacious*					
cious						*practician*						*capricious*					
spacious						*tactician*						*suspicious*					
gracious						*patrician*						*judicious*					
audacious						*musician*						*fallacious*					
precious						*mortician*						*salacious*					
anxious *						*dietician*						*specious*					

Read and pronounce - 'i' before 'e' explained!

We have seen how the letters **ci** followed by both an **a** or an **o** can make the letters **ci** say **sh**: opti**ci**an, vi**cio**us. The letters **ci** followed by an **e** also say **sh**. Listen to the following words: profi**cie**nt, defi**cie**nt, suffi**cie**nt, effi**cie**nt, an**cie**nt.

We also know that the letters **ea** can make the long sound e as in p**ea**ce. The letters **ie** can also make the same sound: piece, yield, field, niece, chief. Sometimes we need to use **ie** to make the e sound after the letter **c** but when we do this the sound is wrong. Look at the following spelling mistake: **cieling**. Now look at the words **proficient** and **deficient** then read the spelling mistake again. Yes! It says sheeling! The following words are common errors: recieve = resheeve, decieve = desheeve, percieve = persheeve.

To stop this happening after **c** we swap the letters around. That is why we say "**i** before **e** except after **c**". These are the proper spellings of the words: **receive, deceive, perceive**.

Day							Day							Day						
Month							Month							Month						
Spell	**ie** and **ei**						Spell	**tion**						Spell	**ci + vowel say sh**					
ceiling							unction							eff icient						
niece							function							suff icient						
receive							suction							in efficient						
field							des truction							in sufficient						
conceive							affection							mal icious						
yield							in spection							del icious						
conceit							protection							musician						
wield							collect							ancient						
deceive							collection							proficient						
chief							connect							deficient						
perceive							connection							at rocious						
Sheffield							correction							precocious						

Other Information

Coach:

The letters ph say f.

This is another very simple rule. It tends to be found in words, the sight of which, alarm students when there is little need.

Listen to the sound made by the letters **ph** in the word **graph**. Demonstrate the rule on scrap paper before beginning the exercise.

Follow the column guides. Speak clearly.

Day						
Month						
Pro						
photo						
sulphur						
lymph						
phantom						
awning						
Philip						
phil an thropy						
philistine						
metaphor						
phosphate						
aphorism						
sulphate						

Day						
Month						
Spell			* Beware !			
ceiling *						
receive *						
deceive *						
conceive *						
perceive *						
thief						
piece						
niece						
field						
yield						
chief						
thieves						

Day						
Month						
Spell						
sulphur						
phantom						
photo						
met aphor						
phil istine						
photograph						
phosphate						
lymph						
lym phatic						
oph thalmic						
dolphin						
alph abet						

Other Information

Coach:

Silent Letters.

We have come across silent letters before. In this exercise they have been highlighted, once more, in blue print.

Inform your student of the silent letter before you begin the relevant columns.

Day							Day							Day						
Month							Month							Month						
Pro	silent h and t						Pro	silent b						Pro	silent w and t					
while							debt							wrist						
which							plumber							wrestle						
white							climb							wrong						
whistle							comb							whose						
rhapsody							succumb							who						
what							numb							wrangle						
where							thumb							wrap						
when							dumb							sword						
castle							lamb							wreck						
whether							climber							wretch						
wheel							numbness							wrench						
whelk							crumb							writhe						
whale							limb							thistle						

Day						Day						Day					
Month						Month						Month					
Spell	silent h					Spell	silent b					Spell	silent w				
while						debt						wrist					
which						plumber						wrestle					
white						climb						wrong					
whistle						comb						whose					
rhapsody						succumb						who					
what						numb						wrangle					
where						thumb						wrap					
when						dumb						wrapped					
whist						lamb						wreck					
whether						climber						wretch					
wheel						numbness						wrench					
whelk						crumbs						written					

Read and Pronounce: Introducing silent k

Many of our words have Latin roots. Latin was the language of the Romans. The silent

b in the word debt has been kept in recognition of the Roman word **debitum**. Some

words have a silent k, like knee, knock, knife, and know. The word know has two silent

letters and we can see them again in the word knowledge. Knowledge also

carries the silent d which dams the power of the final silent e. To know something is to have

knowledge. Knowledge of how words were spoken many years ago tells us that the

silent k was once spoken and in Germany, where we still share many of the same words,

the **k** is still spoken. The more we know about our language the easier it is to use.

Good spelling is not about whether we know the shape of words; it is about knowing the

structures and rules of words and sometimes their history. Poor spelling cannot be

improved by giving students long lists of strange words to remember. You might as well

ask them to remember a list of telephone numbers. Spelling must be taught. Spelling is a

skill to be learned and not an exercise in memory training.

Other Information

Coach:

The letters al can say or.

If we change the letters **al** in the word b**al**l for the letters **or** we still achieve the right sound for the word.   In many words the letters **al** make the sound we associate with the word **or.**

Follow the column guides. Speak clearly.

Day								Day								Day							
Month								Month								Month							
Pro								Spell								Spell							
talk								talk								talkative							
talking								talked								thunderball							
walk								talking								while							
walking								walking								which							
chalk								stalking								call							
all								chalk								calling							
ball								ball								falling							
tall								stall								called							
fall								mothball								thumb							
call								squall								numb							
stall								install								crumb							
hall								hall								hallway							

Other Information

Coach:

The letters ch say k or ck.

This is another very simple rule which is easy to teach. Listen to the sound **ch** in the word me**ch**anic.

They make the sound and act like the letters ck. The word **loch** and **lock** sound exactly the same. These letters are found in words which have joined ours from Greek.

The letters ique

In the following letters found at the end of words which have been imported from French, the **i** takes the long sound of the letter **e** and the **q** takes its normal sound which is **k**. The remaining letters **ue** are silent. We are therefore left with the following sound: **eek** as in **leek**; **uneek** = **unique**.

Demonstrate these sounds to your students and begin the exercise.

Follow the column guides. Speak clearly.

Day						Day						Day					
Month						Month						Month					
Pro						Pro						Spell					
anarchy						unique						*graph*					
chemist						graphic						*graphite*					
anchor						telegraph						*knife*					
knee						oblique						*knit*					
knife						photograph						*knitting*					
chord						clique						*knot*					
chemical						Delphic						*unique*					
chronicle						antique						*oblique*					
synchronize						pique						*pique*					
mechanic						anarchist						*antique*					
mechanism						mystique						*Mo zam bique*					
atmosphere						stomach						*stom ach*					

Other Information

Coach:

The sound of a after u and a after w.

In the exercise on pages 96 and 97, we learned that **a** after **w** makes the same sound as **o** in d**o**g.

Wash and **cosh** are rhyming words. We also learned that **u** and **w** could make the same sound because they have been substituted for each other in many words.

Therefore an **a** after a **u** can also say **o** as in d**o**g.

Listen to the sound in the following words:

sq**ua**d, q**ua**lity.

Demonstrate this rule to your student and then begin the exercise.

Follow the column guides. Speak clearly.

Day							Day							Day						
Month							Month							Month						
Pro							Spell							Spell						
was							*was*							*squash*						
squad							*squad*							*squashed*						
ward							*squad ron*							*squeeze*						
quality							*knee*							*quadratic*						
quadratic							*kneel*							*quality*						
squadron							*equal*							*qualified*						
equal							*equality*							*unique*						
equality							*squalid*							*antique*						
squash							*swan*							*squat*						
squander							*squander*							*quan tum*						
squalid							*squandered*							*quantify*						
what							*qualify*							*quad rant*						

Other Information

Coach:

The letters ur can say ur as in turn.

Listen to the sound of **ur** in the words **burn** and **turn**. Familiarise your student with that sound. Listen to the sound the same letters make after a silent **o:**

colour

vigour

favour

The **ur** makes the same sound as **er** in butt**er** which is little more than a grunt. The **ur** makes the same sound in the word s**ur**prise.

Follow the column guides. Speak clearly.

Day							Day							Day						
Month							Month							Month						
Pro							Spell							Spell						
turn							*threat*							*curd*						
turmoil							*peasant*							*turmoil*						
curd							*pleasant*							*hurdle*						
burn							*pheasant*							*surprise*						
spurn							*emphatic*							*spurn*						
spurned							*unique*							*furnish*						
occur							*kneeling*							*furniture*						
surprise							*knives*							*nurture*						
spur							*knitting*							*occur*						
furnish							*leading*							*lurch*						
furniture							*pleading*							*spurned*						
nurture							*antique*							*burned*						
aphorism							*talk ative*							*church*						

..Day		silent o		Day		silent w		Day		silent h	
Month				Month				Month			
Pro				Spell				Spell			
colour				sword				when			
flavour				answer				whelk			
honour				hollow				whale			
famous				mellow				wheeze			
obvious				written				whisk			
devious				write				whisper			
previous				wrote				whether			
callous				wreckage				rhubarb			
valour				knowledge				white			
candour				Norwich				whiff			
nervous				flowing				whim			
rancour				bellow				while			

Day							Day							Day						
Month							Month							Month						
Spell							Spell	ea as in head						Spell	ea as in heal					
colour							head							heal						
flavour							dread							meal						
honour							threat							peace						
famous							threaten							peaceful						
obvious							breakfast							please						
devious							thread							lease						
previous							spread							release						
callous							meadow							leaf						
valour							pheasant							leaves						
candour							pleasure							plead						
nervous							treasure							mean						
rancour							deadly							clean						

Read and Pronounce

The previous owner of the car was devious to say the least. It was obvious from the start that the colour was not original. The benefit of the doubt was given. However, a closer look would have revealed many flaws which would have been identified by a qualified mechanic. The clutch was worn and the upholstery torn. The gear-box crunched and the engine spewed oil on the drive. The **radiator** leaked, the steering was loose and the whole thing reeked of diesel fumes. It came to grief when the engine **seized**. When it caught fire it was a great relief. No one grieved! The driver was pleased to see the end of it. The deceitful previous owner compounded his deception by not **declaring** that the car had been 'written off' previously after failing to pass its M.O.T. All of which goes to prove that there is little honour in the motor trade. Philanthropists are few and far between and it is easy to declare their virtues when the poor are not in a position to be charitable. Fate always favours the wealthy, or so it seems. Certainly, those people who can afford new cars are less likely to succumb to the miseries of breakdowns and minor infringements of the law with regard to safety regulations. There is much to be said for bicycles and you don't pay road tax.

Day											Day						Day							
Month											Month						Month							
Pro											Spell		**ie not after c**				Spell		**soft g**					
German											*ceiling*						*German*							
Gerald											*thief*						*Gerald*							
gentle											*thieves*						*gentle*							
general											*relief*						*general*							
gender											*relieve*						*gender*							
agent											*deceit*						*agent*							
page											*deceive*						*page*							
outrage											*brief*						*outrage*							
fragile											*piece*						*outrageous*							
gorge											*chief*						*gorge*							
gorgeous											*mischief*						*gorgeous*							
contageous											*conceit*						*engaged*							
outrageous											*conceive*						*fragile*							

Day						Day						Day					
Month						Month						Month					
Spell	**soft g**					Spell	**soft sion**					Spell	**hard sion**				
ingest						profess						invasion					
magistrate						profession						occasion					
rage						confess						division					
huge						confession						explosion					
refuge						express						illusion					
stage						expression						fusion					
ridge						tension						confusion					
bridge						pension						vision					
badge						suspension						provision					
budge						expulsion						television					
grudge						mission						precision					
allergy						passion						ad hesion					

Day					Day					Day				
Month					Month					Month				
Spell	tion				Spell	tion				Spell	cian cial			
induction					*addition*					*patrician*				
seduction					*education*					*optician*				
intention					*nutrition*					*official*				
completion					*election*					*special*				
selection					*attention*					*facial*				
traction					*mention*					*magician*				
extraction					*suction*					*unofficial*				
liquidation					*sanction*					*tactician*				
revolution					*protection*					*politician*				
solution					*pet ition*					*racial*				
junction					*habitation*					*electrician*				
complete					*sen sation*					*politician*				

Day		Day		Day	
Month		Month		Month	
Pro	ch saying c and ph say f	Spell		Spell	*Note! arch = ark
chemist chemistry		chemist		Randolph	
pharmacy pharm acist		chemical		dolphin	
architect archi tecture		chemistry		arch itect *	
phleg matic phone		phone		honour	
phonetic emphasis		phonetic		flavour	
emphatic empha size		phrase		savour	
phrase morpheme		chrome		colour	
chron icle chrome		cholesterol		devious	
anchor anchor age		chloride		previous	
choles terol philat elist		pamphlet		obvious	
oph thalmic synch ronize		emphasis		serious	
physics physical		physical		perilous	
orchid orphan		orchid		orphan	

Read and Pronounce

Ralph, the obese philatelist, had a high level of cholesterol in his blood, a problem which he shared

with Randolph, the eccentric philosopher, whose whole nutritional philosophy placed little emphasis on

the physical but a great deal of weight was placed on the the plate. Never a metaphysical chip ever

passed his lips without it being covered with a sauce. The flavour, when savoured, was an obvious

source of his physician's remorse. However, it wasn't the grease that made him obese. It was sitting

at ease and eating cheese without taking regular exercise. Aristotle and Plato never ate a potato or a

tomato. Centuries later, audacious explorers led expeditions and explorations. They discovered these

plants and made a decision to bring them home. They also discovered a plant called 'tobacco' which,

smells quite awful but much worse it has killed, and is still killing, millions of people.

It was Christmas in the pool. Two dolphins jumped and played the fool. Chlorinated and restricted; their

health suffered as predicted. Elephants are pachyderms; so are mammoths too. Rhinos are relatives but

not the humble shrew. Although they are mammals they are not so large and will not cause a panic

should they ever charge. "Thick skinned" is a metaphor never used for those, whose tendency for

tearfulness makes them lachrymose.

Day		Day		Day	
Month		Month		Month	
Spell	cie says soft sh	Spell	cious	Spell	U is the guard
ancient		gracious		guide	
efficient		spacious		guilt	
efficiency		men dacious		Guinness	
sufficient		at rocious		guitar	
sufficiency		pre cocious		guess	
proficient		del icious		guestroom	
proficiency		precious		guard	
deficient		lo quacious		guarantee	
deficiency		viv acious		guile	
cons cience		per nicious		league	
outrageous		sus picious		vague	

Day						Day						Day					
Month						Month						Month					
Spell	ew					Spell	au - aw					Spell	wa - qua				
Andrew						mauled						swapped					
mildew						hauled						thwart					
pewter						haulage						swarm					
New haven						jaunt						wallaby					
Dewsbury						gaunt						swallow					
crew						back ward						qualify					
stewed						for ward						qualified					
strewn						awk ward						squandered					
news						sprawl						squashed					
brewery						drawn						equality					
sinew						ward						squabble					

Read and Pronounce		Read and Pronounce	
Patricia and Peter Murphy		And far, far, far away	
Stood behind the bar		A football match was played	
Of the Regent Public House		And each result would catapult	
Known both wide and far.		The throng into affray	
Philosophers and painters		No synthesis of emphasis	
Philanthropists and fools		No other topics mooted	
Circumlocuted frequently		Only that of referees	
One subject ever ruled:		And players foully booted.	
The round one known as football		With thickened epidermis	
Engaged the merry throng.		And screaming decibels	
No one was ever offside!		Contentious quotes	
No one was ever wrong!		From belligerent throats	
And in the modest backroom		Were violently upheld	
Strange practices held sway:		But now alas the game is 'up'	
Ancient rites with bones and flights		And no one calls the tune	
As talismans were laid		The pub once called the Regent	
		Is now the Brigadoon.	

Read and Pronounce as many times as you like!

Dear Student and Coach,

If you have reached this point you will be aware that your **journey** through some of the mechanisms, rules, and sounds of our language is nearly over. You have advanced slowly but surely to a level where you are in command of the language. There is a long way to go but you have completed the most difficult sections. Nothing can stop you now.

There must have been times when you have disliked the author for his lack of clarity or for moving too quickly. You may have felt the frustration that all learners of our language have felt. You may have felt anger because you have not been taught the rules earlier. You know them now!

Allow me to apologise for my mistakes; my lack of clarity and the omissions of which there are many but be **assured**: you have now acquired the tools needed for the study of all subjects. Your struggle will help me to improve The Word Wasp so that other students who share your problems will benefit. Be sure to finish all the dotted words in the earlier exercises.

I have one more request to make of you: spread the word! We all have something to learn!

I am grateful to you both for your hard work and your determination.

Harry Cowling - Author.

P.S. Just how painful did you find The Word Wasp's sting? Please write and let me know.

Allow your student to read the following recipe before you dictate it.

Take one page and a willing vessel;

Phonemes and diphthongs;

Slide them together and stir with the aid of a pen.

Heat them with the rude rules.

Revise, remember and rejoice.

Melt the frozen sounds with the heat of the eyes.

While lifting them into the light of learning,

Season with reason

And consume.

Good Luck!

Notes

Notes

Notes